INTERFACIN...
COMPAT...

CW00430172

Other Titles of Interest

Preface

The IBM PCs and compatibles have become firmly established as the "standard" business computers over the past five to ten years. They have also become popular for other types of computing, including various scientific and technical applications at one end of the spectrum, and games at the other. One reason for their widespread use is undoubtedly their versatility. Even if a basic PC is not well suited to a particular application, adding an expansion card plus one or two peripherals will probably remedy the situation. A PC can handle practically any computing task, with only those applications that require massive computing power being "off-limits". Advances in PC technology and software over recent years have resulted in this "off-limits" category steadily shrinking.

For someone who is interested in home constructed add-ons for computers a PC is an attractive proposition. A PC offers plenty of computing power and lots of scope for adding in your own circuits. Furthermore, the prices of PCs seem to drop ever lower. In so-called "real terms", a good PC system probably costs less than most eight bit systems of around ten years ago, but is in a totally different league. Of course, there are other sixteen bit computers which offer plenty of power at low cost, but these tend to be awkward from the interfacing point of view. In fact the interfacing potential of some 16 bit computers seems to be virtually nil. A PC with its expansion slots is the only obvious candidate as the successor to eight bit computers such as the BBC Model B and Commodore 64, which have been popular with electronics enthusiasts for many years.

This book shows you how parallel input/output ports, analogue to digital converters, and digital to analogue converters can be interfaced to the PC expansion bus. Using the principles outlined here it should be possible to interface any circuit (within reason) to the PC expansion bus. The example circuits are all tried and tested types using real components, not theoretical circuits using hypothetical components. They can therefore act as the basis of your PC interfacing projects. A detailed knowledge of interfacing techniques has not been assumed, but the reader should be familiar with basic electronic construction techniques. It is also assumed that the reader is familiar with the basics of running a PC, simple BASIC programming, etc. Building your own PC interfacing projects is not particularly difficult, but it is not really the right starting point for a complete beginner either.

R. A. Penfold

Contents

Page

Chapter 1

PC BASICS

Some of the popular eight bit computers of a few years ago came equipped with a user port and (or) some sort of expansion port that provided an easy means of connecting do-it-yourself add-ons. Modern sixteen bit computers are generally somewhat less accommodating. User ports seem to be non-existent on sixteen bit computers, and proper expansion ports are by no means a universal feature. Despite this, sixteen bit machines do have some potential for the electronic hobbyist, scientist, etc., who needs to use a computer in measurement and control applications. The IBM PCs and compatibles are probably more accommodating in this respect than any other popular sixteen or thirty-two bit computers.

There is no true PC equivalent to the user port of eight bit computers such as the BBC Model B and the Commodore 64. These user ports are basically eight bit parallel ports with each line individually programmable as an input or an output. Additionally there are two handshake lines, plus two sixteen bit timer/counters. This type of port makes it very easy to interface a wide range of circuits to the computer. The nearest PC equivalent to this is a parallel input/output card added into one of the expansion slots. Such cards are produced commercially (but can be a bit difficult to track down). They can, of course, be home constructed if you are not daunted by the prospect of tackling do-it-yourself double-sided printed circuit boards.

Slot Machines

The PCs do have something broadly comparable to the expansion ports of the popular eight bit computers. This is in the form of the vacant expansion slots within the computer, which from the electrical point of view are very similar indeed to traditional expansion ports. Physically they are clearly a rather different proposition. A normal expansion port consists physically of a multi-way connector on the exterior of the

1

computer. Only one add-on at a time can be fitted to the port unless some form of expansion system is used. Normally the add-on simply plugs straight onto the port, or it connects to it via a multi-way cable terminated in a suitable connector. This second method is the one that is generally the easier to implement, and is the one I tend to favour for do-it-yourself add-ons.

With the PC there is no need for any expansion units to accommodate several user add-ons. With most PCs there are three or more free expansion slots for this type of thing. Multi-function cards can help to keep a reasonable number of slots free on a computer that must be well equipped with ports, etc. It is only fair to point out that some PCs, particularly some of the very small types, do not have many free slots once they have been equipped with the bare necessities for normal PC computing. If you are interested in do-it-yourself PC inter-facing there is a lot to be said for a traditional PC case and motherboard, with lots of free slots and space inside the case.

Having the add-on cards inside the computer has its advantages and drawbacks. On the plus side, there is no need to worry about connecting cables getting broken. Neither is there any problem with units fitted on the back of the computer getting in the way, or becoming accidentally detached. Units that mount direct onto expansion ports at the rear of computers are notorious for crashing the computer if they should be accidentally knocked. In fact one or two units of this type have a reputation for crashing the computer if you should happen to breathe too hard near them! With the cards mounted securely inside the computer there is no real problem with unreliability even if the computer should take a few knocks.

The main drawback from the do-it-yourself point of view is that any add-on circuit must be on an accurately made double-sided printed circuit board of irregular shape. This should be fitted with a metal mounting bracket so that the board can be firmly bolted in place. Unfortunately, the metal mounting bracket has a fairly elaborate shape which makes it a bit tricky for home construction. Connections to the outside world are via connectors mounted at the rear edge of the printed circuit board.

2

In order to tackle this type of thing you need to have a fair amount of experience at electronics construction, and a fair degree of expertise. There are ways of making things a little easier though. If you do not feel competent to etch and drill your own double-sided printed circuit boards, or simply do not have the necessary facilities to handle this type of thing, there are companies that can produce prototype boards if you can provide them with reasonable artwork for the board design. However, having one-off boards made can be quite expensive. Whether or not this method is practical depends on how much you are prepared to pay, and on what sort of deal you can negotiate with a printed circuit manufacturing company. For this type of thing a small company is likely to be a better bet than one which normally produces a few thousand boards at a time.

Proprietary Cards
An alternative approach is to use a proprietary printed circuit board rather than a custom type. Ordinary stripboards, etc., are not much use in this context, where a double-sided edge connector is needed to make the connections to an expansion slot. It is actually possible to make up an edge connector to fit an expansion slot, and to fit this onto a piece of stripboard. The edge connector should be fitted with pins so that you can easily make connections from the connector/slot to the stripboard. In theory you can easily make up prototype circuits on the stripboard, and wire them to the expansion slot. The system is reusable in that fresh pieces of stripboard can be fitted to the new connector when new circuits must be developed. Connections to the outside world can be made via a connector fitted on the stripboard, or by way of a flying lead (the latter probably representing the more practical solution).

While this all sounds fine in theory, and will work to some extent in practice, it is a method which I have found to be less than perfect. The main problem is that modern stripboard is not particularly tough, and in fairness it must be said that it is not intended for this type of use. This method tends to be frustrating and expensive, as the stripboard tends to break at the join with the edge connector. If you decide to adopt this method you therefore need to proceed with caution, and must treat the board/connector assembly with the proverbial "kid gloves". This method has to be regarded as considerably less than ideal for either prototyping purposes or finished cards.

What is probably a better approach is to use one of the proprietary prototyping cards which are specifically designed for PC prototyping (but which are also suitable for final units). A major problem with these is that they do not seem to be very widely available in the U.K. Also, those that are available tend to be quite expensive. They vary in sophistication from simple double-sided boards with no electronics, through to boards which have buffers, an address decoder, breadboards, etc. For most do-it-yourself enthusiasts only the simple boards are a practical proposition, as anything beyond this tends to be prohibitively expensive. Even simple prototyping boards (at the time of writing this) cost around twenty pounds or more.

A range of three PC prototyping boards are available from Maplin Electronic Supplies Limited, and these would seem to offer the best value of the few boards of this type currently on offer. The three boards are a half length eight bit type (which is actually about two-thirds of the length of a full size board), and full size eight and sixteen bit boards. They are all made from strong fibreglass, and have standard PC edge connectors to which double-sided pads are connected. The main part of each board is covered with holes/pads on a 0.1 inch matrix. Bus bars for power lines are included around the edge of each board, but apart from this the pads are not linked in stripboard fashion. There is a cluster of pads for a 25-way (right angle) D type connector at the rear of each board. This provides a convenient route to the outside world. All the holes in these boards are through-plated incidentally.

Presumably the boards are made for use with wire wrapping techniques, but simple prototype circuits can be patched together using pieces of thin insulated hook-up wire to interconnect the component leadouts and pins in the correct fashion. Either way results are not likely to be very neat, but prototyping cards are designed to permit circuits to be quickly and easily checked. They are not designed to give neat or pretty results. If neat cards are required, then there is probably no realistic alternative to transferring the designs to custom printed circuit boards.

DIY Proto-Cards

Of course, it is quite possible to build for yourself something comparable to these ready made prototyping cards. However, I think that even if you are fairly expert at making double-sided printed circuit boards it would be necessary to settle for a simplified version of a proprietary board. One problem is simply that it could take weeks to manually drill the thousands of holes in one of these cards! Having the holes through plated is useful, but is probably not something for the do-it-yourself board maker to bother with.

An approach to home produced prototype boards that I have found useful is to have an edge connector which does not have any pads connecting to terminals that will, in all probability, never be needed for any of your prototype circuits. The functions of the various terminals on the edge connector, plus their relative importance, is something that will be discussed more fully later in this chapter. However, it is fair to say that less than half of these terminals actually need to be used for most do-it-yourself expansion cards. Leaving out some of the "fingers" of the edge connector does not actually simplify things very much, but not having to bother with the tracks and pads which would otherwise connect to them can help simplify things a great deal.

On the main part of the board it is probably best to settle for some d.i.l. clusters to take integrated circuits, including one or two 40 pin types to accommodate the larger integrated circuits which are a feature of so many computer add-ons. Remember that if you use 20 and 40 pin clusters, between them these will also accommodate most other sizes of integrated circuit, albeit with some pads left unused. Each pad of each cluster can connect to a row of pads, and some rows of stripboard style pads can be used to provide a general prototyping area for discrete component amplifiers, oscillators, or whatever.

Even using this approach there will be a large number of holes to drill, but nothing like as many as would be needed if the entire board was covered with holes on a 0.1 inch matrix.

You can actually eliminate most of the hole drilling by leaving the main part of the board blank. You can then bolt onto this area a piece of stripboard, or any form of general purpose prototyping board. This includes solderless breadboards, which are perfectly suitable for most PC prototype circuits (but which are obviously not really appropriate to finished units). A card of this type enables new circuits to be rapidly checked and (hopefully) perfected, and can be used over and over again.

For the ultimate in convenience when PC prototyping you can build a card along the lines just described, but include an address decoder on the card. This avoids having to make up an address decoder each time you test a new circuit, and keeps things as quick and simple as possible. This is certainly the type of prototyping card I favour, and is the one I normally use when checking PC prototype circuits. Ideally the address decoder should have several outputs representing different address ranges, or it should be switchable between several address ranges. This enables prototype circuits to be set so that they will not conflict with any user add-ons already in the computer. Address decoding is discussed later in this book.

A variation on this theme is to add an address decoder onto a proprietary PC prototyping card. Connect pins to the pads that connect to important terminals of the edge connector so that connections can be easily made to these lines. If you do not like the idea of prototyping circuits direct onto the board, simply fit it with stripboard, a couple of breadboards, or whatever. This arrangement gives you a very versatile prototyping system, and avoids the need to make up a difficult double-sided printed circuit board. I suppose that you could even make up finished circuits on stripboard or some similar proprietary board, mount it on a ready made PC prototyping card, and then wire it to the edge connector. This would not give the neatest of results, but it should work well enough in practice.

If you require the simplest means of PC interfacing, the obvious approach is to have an edge connector to fit the expansion bus, with a ribbon cable connected to this. Your add-on circuits can then be connected to the opposite end of this cable, and situated outside the PC. They can be bread-boarded, constructed on stripboard, or built using any desired method. This is the PC equivalent to the method used for most do-it-yourself add-ons for eight bit computers. Unfortunately, in my experience at any rate, this system has proved to be a bit unreliable when applied to PC add-ons. The problem is presumably due to the higher clock frequencies used for PCs, especially the "turbo" PCs which are now the norm.

It would be wrong to say that this method is totally imprac-tical, but it can be difficult to get it to work reliably in practice. The chances of it working with a long connecting cable are small, and the shorter the cable, the better the chances of success. The slower the bus speed the greater the chances of reliable operation. Some computers have a "jumper" on the motherboard which can be used to select a slow or a fast expansion bus clock frequency (or there may be a setting in the ROM BIOS setup program of an AT type computer). With some computers, especially XT types, the expansion bus speed is dependent on the main system clock frequency. Switching from the "turbo" mode to the normal one will then slow down the expansion bus. You may have both options available, permitting a very slow expansion bus speed if the normal system clock and slow bus clock frequencies are selected.

There can be paradoxes with this system in that it might fail to work properly with something like a 12 MHz XT com-puter, but might work quite well with a 33 MHz 80386 PC. This is simply due to the wide variation in expansion bus speeds, with the system clock and effective expansion bus speeds being very different in many cases. With a 12 MHz XT the effective expansion bus clock rate may well be something in the region of 12 MHz, but with a 33 MHz 80386 or 80486 computer it will certainly not be anything approaching the system clock frequency. With my 33 MHz 80386 PC the expansion bus can be switched between about 6 MHz and 8 MHz, and it seems to work better with the cable and connec-tor method than does my 10 MHz XT. With a short cable and slow expansion bus frequency selected, this method can probably be made to work with any PC. However, you may

7

feel that these restrictions make this method of working impractical.

The Expansion Buses
Many aspects of PC computing have developed substantially over the years, and the expansion bus is no exception. The original PC/XT bus is an eight bit type. This may seem strange, since the PCs are sixteen and thirty-two bit computers. However, the 8088 microprocessor used in the original PCs (and many clones even today) is a so-called "cut down" version of the 8086 microprocessor. This basically just means that it has a eight bit data bus and must take in data and output it eight bits at a time. Operations on sixteen bit chunks of data are effectively accomplished using two eight bit instructions rather than a single sixteen bit one. Once data is inside the microprocessor's internal registers it is handled as sixteen bit chunks, and internally the 8088 is a true sixteen bit microprocessor. This gives some speed disadvantage compared to the 8086, but the speed difference in practical applications is not very large. Although the 8088 has an eight bit bus, because it is a proper sixteen bit component in other respects, the PCs that are based on this chip are usually regarded as sixteen bit machines rather than superior eight bit types.

It is worth mentioning that some XT class PCs do actually have an 8086 microprocessor. Despite this, they usually retain the standard eight bit expansion bus in order to give full compatibility with 8088 based XT type PCs. Not many PCs based on the 8086 have been produced, and certain Olivetti and Amstrad PCs are probably the only examples of popular PCs of this type. As far as interfacing 8086 based PCs is concerned, they normally have a fully standard XT type expansion bus, and are therefore interfaced in exactly the same manner as any other XT class PCs.

The first development of the PC expansion bus was the sixteen bit type. This became necessary when AT (advanced technology) PCs came along. They have an 80286 microprocessor which is a full sixteen bit type, complete with a sixteen bit data bus. Presumably it would have been possible to have an ordinary 8 bit expansion bus on these computers, but it would have removed some of the potential advantages of using the 80286. The solution was to retain the standard eight bit bus, but to augment it with some further lines carried on a second edge connector mounted in front of the existing connector. This enables appropriate 8 bit cards to be used with an AT computer, but still enables sixteen bit cards to be used where these offer advantages. This sixteen bit PC expansion bus is often called the "ISA" bus, and "ISA" simply stands for "Industry Standard Architecture".

Note that PC compatibles which are based on the 80386SX sixteen bit microprocessor are basically just AT computers, and are interfaced in the same way. Similarly, PCs that are based on the 80386, 80486SX, and 80486 thirty-two bit microprocessors are essentially AT type PCs. They do usually have a thirty-two bit expansion bus, but in most cases only one slot is of this type. It is normally in the form of a standard sixteen bit PC expansion bus with an extra edge connector mounted in front. This added edge connector carries the extra lines needed for thirty-two bit interfacing. There is no true standard for these thirty-two bit slots though, and they normally only accept memory expansion cards produced specially for each make of computer. These thirty-two bit expansion buses are something that will not be considered further here.

There is actually a standard thirty-two bit PC expansion bus which is the result of agreements between several major manufacturers of PC compatibles. This is the "EISA" ("Extended Industry Standard Architecture") bus. From the physical point of view this is substantially different to the thirty-two bit expansion buses of ISA 80386 and 80486 PCs. It has the normal ISA bus, but an extra connector alongside this provides the additional lines needed for thirty-two bit interfacing. It is a high speed bus which has definite advantages over the standard ISA bus for advanced applications that genuinely require very high speed data transfers. However, for many purposes, including most user add-on applications, the ordinary ISA bus will suffice. The EISA bus is not something we will pursue further here.

There is a fourth type of PC expansion bus, and this is IBM's MCA (Micro Channel Architecture) bus. This is another

9

high speed thirty-two bit type, and is one that is used on the more advanced of IBM's recent PCs. These computers are not really traditional PCs, and are intended to be a sort of new generation of PCs. While they have good software compatibility with ordinary PCs, they are largely incompatible as far as hardware is concerned. Consequently, interfacing to this type of PC really falls outside the scope of this book.

The ISA Bus

The ISA bus has a two by 31 way 0.1 inch pitch edge connector to carry the basic eight bit section of the bus. The female connectors are on the computer's motherboard, while the add-on cards must have a male edge connector. This male edge connector is basically just a protrusion on the card which has the 31 "fingers" of copper on both sides of the board. The extra lines for sixteen bit interfacing are carried by a two by 18 way edge connector mounted in front of the two by 31 way connector. Figure 1.1 gives details of this arrangement, including the standard method of pin numbering used for both connectors.

This is a list of the lines available on the 8 bit expansion bus:

Terminal No.	Function	Terminal No.	Function
A1	—I/O CH CK		
A2	D7	A17	A14
A3	D6	A18	A13
A4	D5	A19	A12
A5	D4	A20	A11
A6	D3	A21	A10
A7	D2	A22	A9
A8	D1	A23	A8
A9	D0	A24	A7
A10	I/O CH RDY	A25	A6
A11	AEN	A26	A5
A12	A19	A27	A4
A13	A18	A28	A3
A14	A17	A29	A2
A15	A16	A30	A1
A16	A15	A31	A0

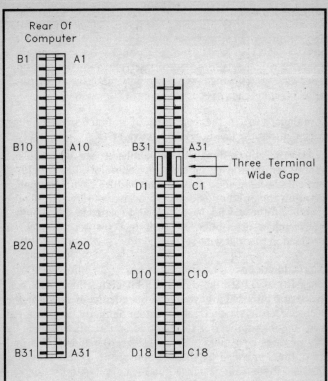

Fig.1.1 The edge connector pin numbering for eight and 16 bit PC buses

Terminal No.	Function	Terminal No.	Function
B1	GND	B11	−MEMW
B2	RESET	B12	−MEMR
B3	+5V	B13	−IOW
B4	IRQ2	B14	−IOR
B5	−5V	B15	−DACK3
B6	DRQ2	B16	DRQ3
B7	−12V	B17	−DACK1
B8	Reserved	B18	DRQ1
B9	+12V	B19	−DACK0
B10	GND	B20	CLK

Terminal No.	Function	Terminal No.	Function
B21	IRQ7	B27	TC
B22	IRQ6	B28	ALE
B23	IRQ5	B29	+5V
B24	IRQ4	B30	OSC
B25	IRQ3	B31	GND
B26	−DACK2		

(A minus sign at the beginning of a function description indicates that the line is negative active.)

Many of these lines will be familiar to anyone who has undertaken interfacing on eight bit computers, and should be particularly familiar to anyone who has dealt with computers based on the 8080 or Z80 microprocessors. However, for the benefit of those who have limited experience of computer interfacing a description of each line (or set of lines) is provided in the following sections.

Data/Address Bus
Lines D0 to D7 are the standard 8 bit bidirectional data bus. Any data provided by your add-on circuits is fed into the microprocessor via these eight lines. Similarly, any data fed from the microprocessor to your add-on circuits will come by way of these eight lines. A0 to A19 are the address bus, and are outputs provided by the microprocessor. These provide a one megabyte address range for memory circuits. Sixteen and thirty-two bit PCs have additional address lines on the second edge connector which enables a much larger amount of memory to be accommodated. However, PCs which have sixteen or thirty-two bit microprocessors normally operate in an 8088 emulation mode where only the basic twenty bit address bus is utilized. These days increasing use of the extended memory of sixteen and thirty-two bit machines is made via disk caches, DOS extenders, etc. This is largely of academic importance to the do-it-yourself add-on enthusiast, and you will normally only need address lines A0 to A19. In fact you will not normally deal with interfacing memory circuits, and will not even need all these address lines.

The address bus is also used for selecting the correct input/output circuit. In this context only the lower sixteen lines (A0 to A15) are utilized. This gives some 64K of input/output address space, or some 65536 input/output addresses in other words. This is more than would ever be needed in a real computer system, and a somewhat simplified approach has therefore been used on the PCs. Only the lower ten address lines (A0 to A9) are utilized, which still gives some 1024 usable input/output addresses. The lower half of the address range is reserved for internal use (i.e. circuits on the motherboard), leaving the upper 512 addresses free for expansion cards. Many of these addresses are reserved for specific functions, such as the standard ports and disk controllers. There is still plenty of space left for your own expansion cards. The input/output map is a topic we will discuss fully later on.

Control Bus
The 8088 microprocessor has a control bus which consists of seven lines. Four of these are MEMR, MEMW, IOR, and IOW, which are all forms of read/write line. Unlike some microprocessors, the 8088 has separate read and write lines, not one line that indicates one type of operation when set high, and the opposite type when set low. Also, the 8088 has separate memory and input/output maps. 8088 based computers do not have input/output devices placed at empty spaces in the memory map, as do computers based on chips such as the 6502 and 68000. Thus, what is a single control line on some microprocessors becomes some four lines on the 8088 series. These lines are all active low. MEMR goes low when the microprocessor is reading from memory — MEMW goes low when it is writing to memory. IOR is activated when data is read from an input device — IOW is activated when data is written to an output circuit. These are obviously important lines which will often have to be decoded by your add-on circuits. Presumably any do-it-yourself add-on cards will not fit in the memory map, but will go into the input/output map. Accordingly, you will not normally need to bother with MEMR and MEMW, but will need to use IOR and IOW extensively.

ALE (address latch enable) is a control line that can be used to synchronise events to microprocessor bus cycles. This is not a line that you will normally need to bother with. The same is not true of AEN (address enable) which goes low during processor bus cycles (i.e. normal operations). It is needed to distinguish between normal bus cycles and DMA (direct memory access) cycles. This must be decoded to the low state by the address/control bus decoder.

The reset line is an output generated by the computer which is a standard active high reset line. This goes high at switch on, or if there is a hardware reset (i.e. if you press the computer's reset button). Software resets, which includes those produced using the keyboard Control Alt Delete sequence, do not normally result in a reset signal being produced on the reset line. It is not essential to use this line to provide the reset signal for your add-on circuits. Some may simply not require a reset signal at all, while with others it might be easier to include a reset pulse generator circuit on the expansion card. In most cases though, where a reset signal is needed it is probably easier to use the computer's reset line. If a negative active reset signal is needed, simply feeding the reset line of the expansion port through an inverter should provide a suitable signal.

DMA/Interrupts
There are nine DMA lines. DACK0 to DACK3 are outputs, as is the TC (terminal count) line. DIRQ1 to DIRQ4 are inputs. These are lines which are only needed for circuits which make use of the advanced DMA facilities. This is not likely to include home constructed expansion cards, and we will consequently not consider the DMA lines further here.

The 8088 has eight normal interrupt lines of the active high variety, but IRQ0 and IRQ1 are not available on the expansion bus. Neither are the special (high priority) interrupt lines such as NMI (non-maskable interrupt). Interrupt lines IRQ2 to IRQ7 are available, but bear in mind that some of these will be used by standard expansion cards such as the serial and parallel ports. For most user add-ons there is no need to utilize the interrupt lines, but they can be useful where it is important that the computer responds to the add-on very rapidly. Applications of this type are usually where data must be read intermittently, but when the data does come along, it does so in large quantities and at a high rate. It is important that each byte of data is read very soon after it has been received, or it may be over-written by the next byte of data. Using the interrupt lines on any computer is a fairly complex business though, and it is much easier to crash the computer than to get it right. Using interrupts on the PCs is perhaps a little less fraught than using interrupts on some of the popular eight bit computers. Even so, this is something that is strictly for the advanced user.

Power and Clocks

The expansion bus includes two clock lines. OSC is a buffered crystal controlled oscillator signal at 14.318 MHz. It is mainly included to act as the clock signal for the colour graphics adaptor, and it is probably not of much use for anything else. The other clock signal is CLK, which is the system clock which has a two-to-one duty cycle. For the original PCs the system clock was at 4.77 MHz, but on modern PC XTs it is normally 8 MHz, 10 MHz, or even higher. On AT class computers the clock frequency can be practically anything from 6 MHz to 50 MHz. Most modern AT type PCs have the ability to operate at a "normal" clock frequency of about 8 MHz, and a "turbo" mode of around 20 MHz to 50 MHz (4.77 MHz and about 8 MHz to 15 MHz for XT class PCs).

Clearly the system clock signal can not be relied upon to be at a certain frequency. On AT computers it may well be missing, with no connection made to this terminal of the expansion bus. These factors must be borne in mind when designing an interface that uses this clock signal. Of course, if you are only producing a card for your own use in a computer where this clock signal is present, and will always be at a certain frequency, then you can design the card on the basis of a known and reliable clock frequency. Remember though, that if you change to a different PC you may have to modify the card in order to get it to function correctly with the new computer. In general it is better to simply ignore both the clock signals on the expansion bus, and where necessary include a suitable clock generator on the expansion card.

Four power supplies plus the 0 volt earth (ground) rail are available on the expansion bus. The available voltages are +5V, −5V, +12V, and −12V. The +5 volt rail should be able to supply several amps without any problems with overloading. It is difficult to be precise about how much power is available on this line as it depends on the rating of the power supply unit, and the current drawn by the motherboard, expansion cards, etc. Some PCs have massive power supplies and hardware which has very modest power requirements. With these there is likely to be well over ten amps of spare current available.

At the other end of the spectrum there are mini-PCs which have relatively low power supply units, and which might have as little as an amp or two to spare for your add-ons. Since your cards are not likely to consume a total of even one amp of current, any PC should be able to power your add-ons without any difficulty. However, it is probably best to use the PC's supply unit only for electronics. If you are using the PC to control electric motors, filament bulbs, etc., then these should have their own power supply units.

The +12 volt supply should also be able to provide an amp or two without any problems. In fact it might be possible to draw as much as 4 amps from the +12 volt line, but it is probably best to stick to a maximum of about 2 amps unless you can definitely ascertain that your computer can reliably supply more than this. On many PCs the +12 volt supply does not seem to be well stabilised, and often seems to be at around +13 volts. I think that I am right in stating that this supply is mainly intended for powering the motors in the disk drives, and that the latter include their own regulator circuits. It is probably not safe to assume that this line is well stabilised, or particularly noise-free.

The ratings of the negative supplies are relatively small. The −5 volt and −12 volt lines are usually rated at 0.3 amps and 0.25 amps respectively (some of which may well be consumed by other cards). It is probably best to keep the current drains from the negative supplies down to about 100 milliamps (0.1 amps) or less. In most applications the negative supplies will not be needed at all, and where they are required it will often only be necessary to draw currents of a few milliamps or less.

For example, the "tail" resistor of some analogue to digital converters requires a negative supply current of well under 1 milliamp, and for a circuit which has a three or four operational amplifiers a negative supply current of less than 10 milliamps would normally be needed.

The Rest

The I/O CH RDY (Input/Output Channel Ready) line is an important one. It is an input which can be used to insert wait states. A wait state is simply a system clock cycle during a read or write operation where nothing happens. The purpose of introducing these "dummy" clock cycles is to slow down the computer to the point where a slow memory or input/output circuit can keep up. This might be necessary for some user add-ons. However, if at all possible it is obviously better to keep things simple by having add-on circuits that can keep up with the computer. In most cases there is no difficulty in doing this, and I/O CH RDY can be ignored.

I/O CH CK (Input/Output Channel Check) is an active low input line. It is taken low in order to indicate that a memory or input/output parity error has occurred. A non-maskable interrupt is then generated. This line is not normally used with user add-ons.

Sixteen Bit Bus

Most do-it-yourself PC interfacing only requires the eight bit bus, but I suppose that there are some applications which would benefit from use of the full sixteen bit bus. This is a list of the extra functions available on the sixteen bit ISA bus.

Terminal No.	Function	Terminal No.	Function
D1	−MEM CS16	D10	−DAQ10
D2	−I/O CS16	D11	DRQ5
D3	IRQ16	D12	−DACK6
D4	IRQ11	D13	DRQ6
D5	IRQ12	D14	−DACK7
D6	IRQ15	D15	DRQ7
D7	IRQ14	D16	+5V
D8	−DACK0	D17	−MASTER
D9	DRQ0	D18	GND

Terminal No.	Function	Terminal No.	Function
C1	BHE	C10	−MEMW
C2	A23	C11	D8
C3	A22	C12	D9
C4	A21	C13	D10
C5	A20	C14	D11
C6	A19	C15	D12
C7	A18	C16	D13
C8	A17	C17	D14
C9	−MEMR	C18	D15

(A minus sign at the beginning of a function description indicates that the line is negative active.)

When a PC is equipped with a sixteen bit bus there are actually a few changes to the basic eight bit bus. −DACK0 for instance, becomes −REFRESH on the sixteen bit bus. −REFRESH simply indicates that a memory refresh cycle is in progress. This is really only of academic importance since it is highly unlikely that you would ever use one of the lines which is subject to these variations of usage. Most of the extra lines on the sixteen bit bus are of no interest to the do-it-yourself interfacing enthusiast. The extra address lines are only needed when accessing extended memory, and are irrelevant to input/output devices. Most of the other lines are interrupt and DMA lines, etc., which you will probably not need to use either.

Of course, the extra data lines (D8 to D15) will be needed for sixteen bit interfacing, and permit data to be exchanged in sixteen bit words rather than being limited to eight bit bytes. BHE is the Bus High Enable output, and it is alternatively known as SBHE (System Bus High Enable). It indicates that data transfer is to be on the high byte (D8 to D15), as well as on the low byte (D0 to D7). Data transfers always involve the lower byte, and so there is no equivalent to this on the eight bit bus. −MEM CS16 and −I/O CS16 are inputs that are used to inform the computer that memory and input/output data exchanges are to be sixteen bit types. If suitable signals are not applied to these inputs, sixteen bit data transfers will be carried out as two eight bits transfers.

18

Important Lines

Clearly a large number of the lines included on the expansion bus will not be needed for most interfacing. The terminals of the edge connector that connect to unused lines can obviously be omitted. This can help to simplify the printed circuit boards if you are using custom printed circuit boards. It can massively simplify things if you are making up your own prototyping boards. This is a list of the terminals of the edge connector that you will often need to implement, and which should certainly be included in PC prototyping systems.

Terminal No.	Function	Terminal No.	Function
A2	D7	A27	A4
A3	D6	A28	A3
A4	D5	A29	A2
A5	D4	A30	A1
A6	D3	A31	A0
A7	D2	B1	0V (GND)
A8	D1	B2	RESET
A9	D0	B3	+5V
A11	AEN	B5	−5V
A22	A9	B7	−12V
A23	A8	B9	+12V
A24	A7	B13	−IOW
A25	A6	B14	−IOR
A26	A5		

This list is basically just the lower ten lines of the address bus, the data bus, the supply lines, RESET, AEN, −IOW and −IOR. For 16 bit interfacing you will normally need these lines as well.

Terminal No.	Function	Terminal No.	Function
D2	−I/O CS16	C14	D11
C1	BHE	C15	D12
C11	D8	C16	D13
C12	D9	C17	D14
C13	D10	C18	D15

Getting Physical

An important aspect of PC interfacing is getting the physical dimensions of the cards spot-on. This is every bit as important as getting things right electronically. Make small errors in certain dimensions and you could find that the card will simply not fit into the computer. Make the edge connector inaccurately and it may well short circuit adjacent pairs of contacts from one end of the expansion slot to the other! This might not actually do any damage to the computer, since most logic circuits are pretty tough, and PC power supplies have comprehensive protection circuits which should avoid catastrophe in the event of short circuits. However, with this type of thing it is best not to find out the hard way. If your PC should prove to be unable to withstand this type of problem, the result could be an extremely expensive repair bill. When undertaking any computer interfacing it is important to proceed very carefully indeed, taking as few risks as possible. The more expensive the computer, the more carefully you need to proceed.

I prefer not to try out prototype cards on my 80286 and 80386 based PCs at all, and instead use an XT class PC that is largely comprised of left-overs from upgrades to my main PCs, plus parts obtained cheaply or in swops with friends. This PC is good enough for most PC interfacing applications, and if the worst should happen it would not be a major loss. A major repair such as fitting a new motherboard would be an unwelcome expense, but it would not "break the bank". I could not say the same of a repair to something like a 33 MHz 80486 based PC. Interfacing to PCs is certainly something I would not recommend for beginners at electronics. For beginners the best advice is to gain some experience building up a few simple electronic projects before trying your hand at any form of computer interfacing. Either that, or you should be prepared to write-off your PC against experience!

Physical details of eight and sixteen bit cards are shown in Figures 1.2 and 1.3 respectively. These are largely self explanatory, but there are a few important points to note. Firstly, the length dimension given for the cards is for full-length cards. Obviously cards do not have to be full-length types, and probably most PC expansion cards are only about

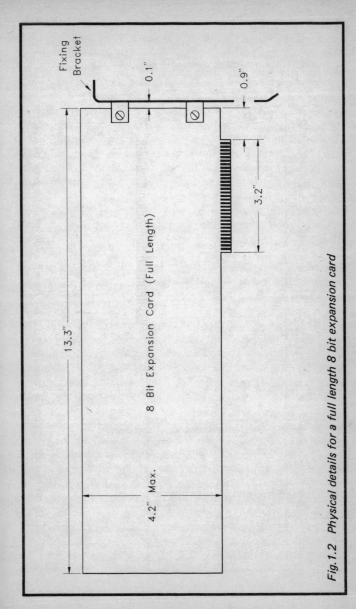

Fig. 1.2 Physical details for a full length 8 bit expansion card

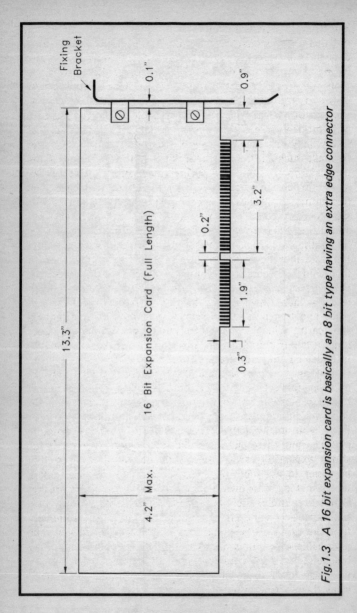

Fig. 1.3 A 16 bit expansion card is basically an 8 bit type having an extra edge connector

Fixing Bracket

0.1"

0.9"

16 Bit Expansion Card (Full Length)

13.3"

4.2" Max.

0.2"

3.2"

1.9"

0.3"

22

half length. There is no minimum acceptable size for PC cards, but there is a practical limitation in that the card must be long enough to include the full edge connector, or both connectors in the case of a sixteen bit card. Of course, if a card is less than full length, it is the front part of the card that is cut down to size. The edge connector and mounting bracket at the rear of the card make it unacceptable to shorten this end. It is probably not a good idea to produce cards that are just fractionally less than full length. It would seem to be better to make such cards full length, so that the front end of the card is properly supported by the guide rails in the computer.

PC expansion cards are generally about 4 inches high (excluding the edge connector). With most computers it is safe to have cards of up to about 4.2 inches in height, but above this you may find the card will fit alright, but that the lid of the case can not be closed properly. With some mini PC cases it is necessary to have cards no more than about 4 inches high. There is no minimum height for PC cards, but there are again practical limitations. If you make cards much under 4 inches high it may be very difficult to slot them in place and to remove them again. I generally make PC expansion cards 4 inches high and a minimum of about 5 inches long, even if this gives an area that is far larger than the interface circuit really requires.

Making your own fixing brackets is a bit tricky, as they are quite an intricate shape. I will not give any details of fixing brackets here, as the best route to making your own is to copy a blanking plate from one of the expansion slots in your PC. You might actually have one or two spare blanking plates, where these plates have been removed to make way for added expansion cards. If so, then it will almost certainly be easier to use these for your home constructed cards than to try making your own brackets. Of course, a fixing bracket is not absolutely essential, and PC cards fit quite firmly into the expansion slots. If the bracket is omitted it is unlikely that the card will be pulled out of place provided you take reasonable care. It is clearly preferable to include mounting brackets, but many constructors of PC expansion cards prefer to simply omit them altogether. I must admit that I avoid using them whenever possible.

Although in Figures 1.2 and 1.3 the mounting brackets are shown as being fitted to the boards via simple right angled brackets, these brackets are often unnecessary. Often PC cards are fitted with right angled D connectors to permit connections to be made to the outside world. In such cases the D connectors will normally provide a convenient means of fixing the mounting bracket to the board. A suitable cutout for the connector must be made in the bracket, and this can be cut using a miniature file or a coping saw.

If you are lucky, you may already have one or two brackets which have cutouts for one or two D connectors. Multi-function cards are often supplied with brackets of this type. These cards often require more sockets than it is possible to accommodate on the rear section of the card. The extra sockets must therefore be mounted on blanking plates for unused expansion slots, and connected to the card via jumper leads. Many PC cases have mounting holes for D connectors in the rear panel of the case. You can then use these instead of the drilled blanking plates, leaving the latter free for use with your own expansion cards. If you make your own mounting brackets, unless you have access to some advanced metal working facilities it will be much easier to use thin (about 18 s.w.g.) aluminium than heavy gauge steel. Whatever means you adopt for mounting the bracket on the expansion card, make sure that it is the correct distance from the rear of the card. Small errors here can make it impossible to fit the card into the computer.

Programming
The hardware of a PC is normally handled via DOS routines, but your home constructed expansion cards will usually be types that have no DOS support. Your only means of reading from them or writing data to them is to directly access the hardware via a suitable programming language. Some languages are better for this type of thing than are others. It is only fair to point out that some PC languages are of no use whatever in this context. They simply do not provide instructions that give direct access to devices in the input/output map.

Obviously there should be no problem when using assembly language or machine code since you have direct access to the instructions of the microprocessor which access the input and output circuits. Some computer languages enable programs to call and run assembly language routines, and this provides a means of controlling user add-ons. This method of handling things is much used with eight bit computers running inter-preted BASICs. These languages almost invariably provide instructions that can be used to control user add-ons, but for some applications they would simply run too slowly. A mix-ture of BASIC and assembly languages give the convenience of the former with the speed of the latter when required. This is a system which I have always found to be very good in prac-tice, but the speed of compiled BASICs for sixteen bit com-puters tends to make it less attractive in a PC context. However, it is an approach which could be well suited to some situations, and it is certainly something worth keeping in mind.

The BASIC supplied with most PC compatibles is Micro-soft's GW BASIC, which is an interpreted BASIC. This makes it easy to use, but it is not fast by PC language standards. On most PCs it is good enough for many applications though, and it is certainly the language I would recommend when initially experimenting with PC add-ons. In GW BASIC the OUT instruction is used to write data to devices in the input/output map (e.g. OUT 768,12 would write a value of 12 to output address 768). Data can be read from devices in the input/ output map using the INP function. For instance, the instruc-tion X = INP(768) would set variable X at the value read from input address 768.

Most other BASICs, whether interpreted or compiled, should work perfectly well with user add-ons. The only exceptions are some of the higher level BASICs which have mouse support, windowing facilities, etc. These often lack facilities for direct accessing of the hardware. The BASIC 2 language supplied with some Amstrad PCs would seem to offer no obvious means of directly controlling the computer's hard-ware, and Microsoft's Visual BASIC is another example of a PC BASIC in this category. A traditional BASIC would seem to be a safer bet than a modern type in the current context.

The abilities of other PC languages to control the computer's hardware seems to vary considerably. Most languages can actually manage this type of thing, but not necessarily in a particularly straightforward manner. If you are not a particularly expert programmer, it is probably best to use a good BASIC language. BASIC is a much maligned language, but any fairly recent version should offer excellent facilities and reasonably fast operating speed. While BASIC is not well suited to all applications, it is very good indeed for measurement and control applications. It is therefore well suited to most applications which involve user add-ons.

Properly Addressed

As explained previously, the input/output map for PCs consists of only 1024 addresses, as only the bottom ten address lines are used for input/output mapping. The lower half of the map is reserved for system hardware (i.e. circuits on the motherboard), while the upper half is reserved for the expansion bus. Standard circuits such as serial and parallel ports do not count as system hardware, since they fit onto the expansion bus. This means that the 512 address range for the expansion bus is fairly crowded, with few gaps. This is the PC input/output map.

System

Hex Address Range	Function
000-01F	DMA Controller #1
020-03F	Interrupt Controller #1
040-05F	8254 Timer
060-06F	Keyboard Interface
070-07F	Real Time Clock
080-09F	DMA Page Register
0A0-0BF	Interrupt Controller #2
0C0-0DF	DMA Controller #2
0F0	Clear Processor Busy
0F1	Reset Processor
0F8 − 0FF	Arithmetic Processor

Expansion Bus

Hex Address Range	Function
1F0-1F8	Fixed Disk
200-207	Games Port
210-217	Expansion Unit

220-24F	Reserved
278-27F	Parallel Port 2
2F0-2F7	Reserved
2F8-2FF	Serial Port 2
300-31F	Prototype Card
320-32F	Fixed Disk
360-36F	Reserved
378-37F	Parallel Port 1
380-38F	SDLC Bisynchronous #2
3A0-3AF	SDLC Bisynchronous #1
3B0-3BF	Monochrome Display/Printer Adapter
3C0-3CF	Reserved
3D0-3DF	Colour Graphics Adapter
3F0-3F7	Floppy Disk Controller
3F8-3FF	Serial Port 1

It might actually be possible to exploit some of the lower
512 addresses for user add-ons, but this would not be doing
things in standard PC fashion, and is best avoided. It could
easily lead to problems. Although the upper half of the
address range is pretty crowded, there are some areas here
which can be exploited for user add-ons. In particular, there
are thirty-two addresses from &H300 to &H31F. These are
reserved for prototype cards, and your own expansion cards
could reasonably be deemed to be in this category. It is
certainly an area of the memory map that you can use without
any real risk of clashes with existing hardware. Thirty-two
addresses is not a great deal when compared to the number
available on some other computers, such as the BBC computers with their two pages (512 addresses) of available
address space on the expansion bus. However, this should be
perfectly adequate for most users. It is sufficient for several
parallel port cards, plus some analogue converter boards, or
whatever.

If thirty-two addresses is deemed inadequate, there are
ways around the problem. Any addresses in the upper half of
the memory map which are not actually occupied by hardware in your computer can safely be used. This statement has
to be qualified somewhat, as the real situation is that addresses
of this type can be used safely by you with your particular PC

system. It can not be assumed that home constructed cards which use these addresses can also be used successfully with other PCs. In practice, provided you use addresses that are reserved for an unusual piece of hardware, it is unlikely that there will be any problems. Something like the address space for the second serial port would not be a wise choice, but using the address space reserved for the SDLC Bisynchronous Port #2 would seem to be a very safe bet. There are actually a few small gaps in the input/output map which do not seem to be allocated to anything, and it would presumably be perfectly alright to exploit one or more of these.

Another means of obtaining more addresses for your add-ons is to use some of the upper address lines that are normally left unused. For instance, you could have some add-ons that use the address space from &H300 to &H31F, but which will only be activated if address line A10 is low. You could have a second piece of hardware using the same address space, but designed to operate only when A10 is high. The first set of hardware would be accessed at addresses from &H300 to &H31F, but the second set of hardware would be at addresses from &H700 to &H71F. I have never found it necessary to adopt this method, but in theory it would enable the basic range of thirty-two addresses to be used many times over, giving more expansion potential than could ever be used in practice.

Finally
This covers the basics of PC interfacing in general terms. Probably the main problem for the do-it-yourself PC add-on enthusiast is that PC interfacing is a bit awkward from the mechanical point of view. However, if you use proprietary PC prototyping cards, or take care to get things accurate when making your own cards, the mechanical aspects of construction should not prove to be insurmountable. In Chapter 2 we will consider electronic circuits for PC address decoding, etc., and this aspect of PC interfacing is normally very straightforward. In fact interfacing to PCs is more straightforward than interfacing to many popular eight bit computers as far as the electronics is concerned. Thankfully, the PC is free from the quirky methods of interfacing used on many 8 bit computers.

Chapter 2

INTERFACING CIRCUITS

When designing PC interface circuits the first task is to produce a suitable address decoder circuit. Although circuits of this type are generally called address decoders, in most cases they also need to decode a few lines of the control bus as well. When you access one of your add-on circuits a certain set of logic states appear on the address bus, and on certain lines of the control bus. This set of logic states should be unique to that particular add-on, and should not occur when any other circuit is being accessed. The purpose of the address decoder is to recognise this set of logic states, and to produce a change in output state while that set of logic levels persists. The output of the address decoder normally holds the data bus of the add-on circuit in an inactive state. However, when it detects the appropriate combination of input levels its change in output state activates the add-on circuit.

Bus Times
The basic way in which the add-on responds depends on whether it is a "read" or a "write" device. If the computer must read data from the circuit, once activated, the add-on's data bus will become a normal set of logic outputs. It is important to get things absolutely right with this type of circuit. If it should be activated at the wrong time, it will probably try to place data onto the data bus at the same time as some other piece of hardware. It might even try to place data onto the data bus at the same time as the microprocessor is writing data. Modern logic circuits are generally quite tolerant of this type of thing, and being realistic about it, the chances of anything being damaged are slight. On the other hand, it is clearly better not to risk any damage to expensive hardware, no matter how small the risk might be. Also, a data bus conflict of this type is almost certain to crash the computer. Continuously crashing and rebooting the computer is a good way to waste a lot of time.

It is also important for things to be just right when writing data to an add-on circuit. The situation is slightly less critical in that when an add-on of this type is activated it reads whatever is on the data bus. If it is activated at the wrong time it will increase the loading on the data bus, but this is not likely to cause any ill effects. The data read by the device will be erroneous though, and the add-on will totally fail to function. A device which only reads from the data bus can obviously not try to force data onto the bus, and in theory at any rate, can not cause any damage or even crash the computer.

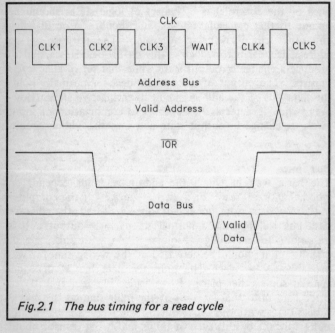

Fig.2.1 The bus timing for a read cycle

Figure 2.1 shows bus timing for a read cycle. The correct address is placed on the address bus some time before valid data from the peripheral circuit must be ready and waiting on the data bus, so that it can be read by the microprocessor. Similarly, −IOR goes low well before data is present on the data bus. This gives time for the address decoder to operate

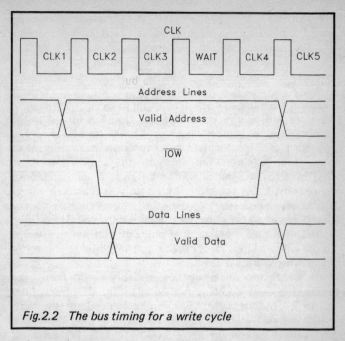

Fig.2.2   The bus timing for a write cycle

and provide an active output level. The timing for a write cycle is shown in Figure 2.2. The main point to note here is that –IOW returns to the high state while valid data is still being placed onto the data bus. This causes the active output signal from the address decoder to cease, and it is this transition which is used to latch the data.

In normal logic circuit terms the address decoder does not need to be particularly fast in operation. Computers, even the faster ones such as some of the more advanced PCs, are simply not that fast in general electronic terms. On the other hand, the address decoder has nanoseconds rather than microseconds in which to work. Ordinary CMOS integrated circuits are not suitable as they are too slow. These components are designed for low current consumption, which is achieved at the expense of very sluggish performance. In any case, these components are not logic compatible with the PC buses. The buses of a PC operate at normal TTL levels. Ordinary 74LS** series devices

31

are well suited to this application as they are both fast and load the buses by acceptable amounts. 74HCT** components are also suitable, but the 74HC** components are not. The 74HC** logic devices operate at CMOS rather than TTL logic levels.

Practical Decoding

Here we will only be concerned with decoders for use in the prototype card address range of &H300 to &H31F. The general principles discussed here apply to interfacing using other address ranges, but obviously the address line states that have to be decoded will be different if another address range is used. As pointed out previously, it is unlikely that it would ever be necessary to use other address ranges, since the thirty-two available addresses from &H300 to &H31F will be sufficient for most needs. It is probably best not to attempt to use other address ranges unless you are absolutely sure you know what you are doing.

If we first consider matters in fairly broad terms, the minimal address decoding needed is to decode address lines A5 to A9. Additionally, AEN must be decoded, together with −IOR and (or) −IOW. These are the states of these lines when an input address in the range &H300 to &H31F is accessed.

Line	Logic State	Line	Logic State
A5	Low	A9	High
A6	Low	AEN	Low
A7	Low	−IOR	Low
A8	High	−IOW	High

For read operations the state of −IOW is irrelevant, and it does not need to be decoded. This gives us the basic read address decoder represented diagrammatically in Figure 2.3. This will respond to any read operation to an input device in the address range &H300 to &H31F, but it should ignore any other read operations, as well as all write types and memory accesses. Most decoders are designed to have an output that is normally high and which goes low when the circuit is activated. Not all peripheral circuits require things this way round though, and where appropriate the decoder must be

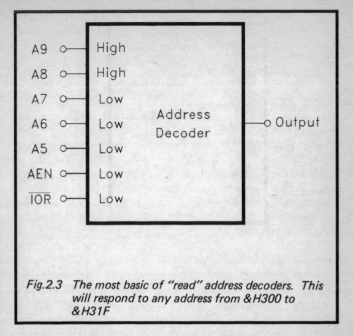

A9 ○——— High

A8 ○——— High

A7 ○——— Low

A6 ○——— Low   Address   ○ Output
                 Decoder

A5 ○——— Low

AEN ○——— Low

$\overline{IOR}$ ○——— Low

*Fig.2.3 The most basic of "read" address decoders. This
will respond to any address from &H300 to
&H31F*

designed to have an output that is normally low, and which
pulses high while it is activated. Remember that in order to
convert a decoder from one type to the other you merely need
to add an inverter at the output.

This is the set of states that must be decoded when an
output circuit in the relevant address range is accessed.

Line	Logic State	Line	Logic State
A5	Low	A9	High
A6	Low	AEN	Low
A7	Low	−IOR	High
A8	High	−IOW	Low

This is the same as before, but the states of −IOR and
−IOW have been reversed. In this case it is −IOR that can be
ignored and −IOW that must be decoded. This basic "write"
decoder is shown diagrammatically in Figure 2.4. When

33

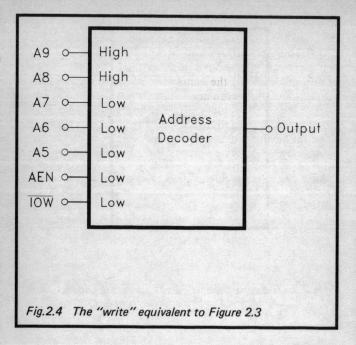

Fig.2.4 The "write" equivalent to Figure 2.3

designing any address decoder or similar logic circuits it is a good idea to write down the decoded state of each line, or produce a diagram of the type shown in Figure 2.4, so that you get a clear picture of what is required. This can help to avoid time consuming errors.

In practice you will not always need an address decoder specifically for a read circuit or a write type. Most practical interfacing applications involve both reading and writing to the peripheral circuit. Even if the purpose of a port is (say) to output eight bit bytes of data, it may well consist of more than just eight output lines. It is often necessary to carefully control the flow of data from the basic eight bit port to some further hardware. This requires one or more handshake lines, one of which will probably be an input to monitor the status of the secondary piece of hardware. A Centronics type parallel printer port is a good example of an eight bit output port of this type. It includes a strobe output which provides a pulse each time a fresh byte of data is placed on the data outputs. It has two handshake inputs ("Acknowledge" and "Busy"), one of which is used to indicate whether or not the printer is ready to receive further data. The correct flow of data into or out of the computer is something you need to consider carefully when undertaking do-it-yourself interfacing. Get this aspect of things slightly wrong, and you may well find yourself having to do a complete redesign and rebuilding job on the add-on card.

One way of tackling the problem of combined read and write address decoding is to produce two separate address decoders, one for each function. This has to be regarded as doing things the hard way, and is also not a strictly valid method of PC interfacing. Each line of the PC expansion bus should be loaded by no more than one 74LS** series TTL input, or an equivalent amount. Using two address decoders would load some lines with two inputs. In practice this would probably not matter too much, and there are ways around the problem. One of these is to add buffers on the relevant lines so that these limit the loading of the bus lines to one 74LS** TTL load. This further adds to the complication and expense of the address decoder though.

In general it is better to produce an all-in-one address decoder of the type depicted in Figure 2.5. With AEN and the five address inputs at the appropriate states, the "Read" output is activated if −IOR is low, and the "Write" output is activated if −IOW is low. While it is quite possible to produce a decoder of this type, in practice it is often easier to have a decoder which does not process −IOR or −IOW. The output of this simple decoder is then fed to a further decoder, which does process −IOW and −IOR. This scheme of things is shown in Figure 2.6. The gate circuit which generates the separate "Read" and "Write" outputs can be very simple indeed. This system is very versatile in that it also provides a combined "read/write" output, which is what is needed for some peripheral chips. This type of decoder is therefore apposite to just about any method of interfacing.

The interface chips that require a combined "read/write" decoder output are the 82** series which are specifically designed for operation with 8080 series microprocessors.

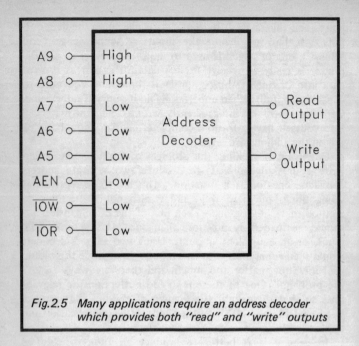

A9	○—	High			
A8	○—	High			
A7	○—	Low			○ Read
A6	○—	Low	Address		Output
A5	○—	Low	Decoder		
AEN	○—	Low			○ Write
IOW	○—	Low			Output
IOR	○—	Low			

*Fig.2.5   Many applications require an address decoder
which provides both "read" and "write" outputs*

There are actually a number of other peripheral chips which
are designed to be bus compatible with the 8080 series of
microprocessors.   These are less common than the 82**
series chips, but you may well encounter some devices of this
type.   These chips are all used in the manner shown in Figure
2.7.   The address decoder only has to process AEN plus
address lines A5 to A9.   −IOR and −IOW are not simply
ignored, but are instead decoded by the appropriate inputs of
the 82** series integrated circuit.

So far we have only considered the situation where a single
input register and one output register are to be used.   The
address decoder has treated the &H300 to &H31F address
range as if it was a single address.   The peripheral circuit
effectively occupies all these addresses, and can be operated
using any address in this range.   This means that no other
devices can exist in this address range, which is obviously a
bit restrictive.   With many of the 82** series chips there are

36

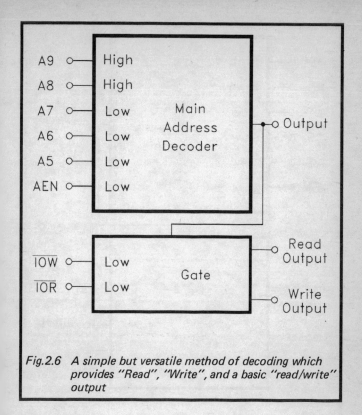

Fig.2.6 *A simple but versatile method of decoding which provides "Read", "Write", and a basic "read/write" output*

several registers, and each chip must therefore occupy several addresses, with a different register located at each address.

This is easily accomplished, as the 82** series integrated circuits which have more than one read/write register have one or more register select inputs. These are simply fed from the address bus, and would normally be fed from the least significant address lines (i.e. A0, A1, etc.). In the example setup of Figure 2.7 there are three register select inputs which are fed from address lines A0 to A2. This table shows the number of registers available for various numbers of chip select inputs.

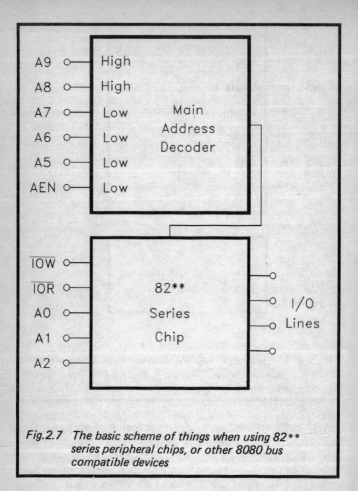

Fig.2.7 The basic scheme of things when using 82** series peripheral chips, or other 8080 bus compatible devices

No. of C/S Inputs	Maximum No. of Registers
0	1
1	2
2	4
3	8
4	16

In the example of Figure 2.7 there are three chip select inputs fed from three address lines. This gives a maximum of eight read registers and eight write types. These registers are at addresses from &H300 to &H308. However, as less than full address decoding is being used, with A3 and A4 being left unprocessed, the full range of thirty-two addresses remain occupied. The eight registers appear again as an echo at addresses &H309 to &H30F. There are further echoes at &H310 to &H318, and &H319 to &H31F. This blocks any further add-ons being used in the &H300 to &H31F address range.

Two 82** series peripheral chips can be used in a set-up of the type shown in Figure 2.8. The two chips are connected to the expansion bus in parallel. We are ignoring the data buses in these address decoding examples, but these would both be connected to the data bus of the expansion bus. The address decoder has two outputs, one for each peripheral chip. These outputs cover different address ranges. In practice this can only be achieved by processing further address lines.

Conventionally, it would be address line A4 that was decoded. One peripheral would be activated when A4 was high, the other would be activated when it was low. This would put the first peripheral device (A4 low) at addresses from &H300 to &H308, and at echoes from &H309 to &H30F. The second peripheral (A4 high) would be at addresses from &H310 to &H318, and at echoes from &H319 to &H31F. By also decoding A3 it would be possible to have four chips. The two extra chips would occupy the address ranges which were previously occupied by echoes. More than four chips having eight registers would not be possible, as this would require more than the available thirty-two addresses. As pointed out previously, there are ways of obtaining greater expansion, but it is unlikely that more than thirty-two read registers and thirty-two write types would be needed.

One slight flaw with this method of using devices in parallel is that some lines of the expansion bus are loaded by more than one input. In particular, the data bus will be loaded by several inputs. This does not necessarily matter in practice,

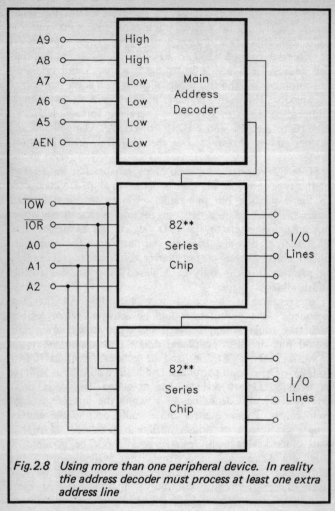

Fig.2.8 Using more than one peripheral device. In reality the address decoder must process at least one extra address line

since there should only be one input in the active state at any one time. The loading is therefore much less than it might at first appear. However, in this sort of situation you can always play safe by including buffers on the lines which might otherwise be excessively loaded.

Gates and Decoders

There is no single solution to address decoding problems, and there are often dozens of different ways of achieving much the same thing. Some solutions are more practical than others. In general, it is better to use simple gates and inverters. These are fast in operation and inexpensive. They do some-times have a disadvantage, which is that it can take a lot of inter-wiring in order to get a few gates and inverters to give the desired action. For a home constructed unit it may be better to opt for more complex devices, such as three to eight line decoders, in order to keep the board layout reasonably simple and straightforward. The more complex decoder integrated circuits can be quite expensive, and are often relatively slow in operation. These may actually be perfectly usable for PC address decoding, but it should be possible to find good ways of handling the decoding without resorting to any of the more exotic 74LS** series of integrated circuits.

The two basic types of logic gate are the AND and OR varieties. Logic gates all have two or more inputs, and a single output. If we consider a simple two input AND gate first, the truth table provided below shows the function it performs.

INPUT 1	INPUT 2	OUTPUT
Low	Low	Low
Low	High	Low
High	Low	Low
High	High	High

Its output is low unless input 1 AND input 2 are high, and it is from this that the AND name is derived. The action is much the same if there are more inputs. With all the inputs high, the output is high. If one or more of the inputs are low, the output is low.

This is the truth table for a 2 input OR gate.

INPUT 1	INPUT 2	OUTPUT
Low	Low	Low
Low	High	High
High	Low	High
High	High	High

The output of a two input OR gate is low unless one OR other of its inputs is high, and it is from this that the OR name is derived. Again, the action of the gate remains much the same if there are more than two inputs. With none of the inputs in the high state the output will be low, but if one or more of the inputs should go high, the output will also go high.

There are a couple of variations on the AND and OR gates, and these are called NAND and NOR gates. These are the truth tables for two input NAND and NOR gates respectively.

INPUT 1	INPUT 2	OUTPUT
Low	Low	High
Low	High	High
High	Low	High
High	High	Low

INPUT 1	INPUT 2	OUTPUT
Low	Low	High
Low	High	Low
High	Low	Low
High	High	Low

These really only differ from the original truth tables in that the output states are reversed. In effect, a NAND gate is an AND gate with its output fed through an inverter. Therefore, if input 1 and input 2 are taken high, the output goes low. Any other set of input states sends the output high. Similarly, a NOR gate is effectively just an OR gate with its output inverted.

There is actually a fifth type of gate, but this is little used in practice. It is the exclusive OR (XOR) gate, which is similar to an OR gate. However, with an OR gate, the output is not only high if input 1 or input 2 is high. If both inputs are taken to the high state, then the output will still go high. With an exclusive OR gate only taking one input high will send the output high. Having no inputs set high, or more than one input set to the high state, results in the output going low. I suppose that this could reasonably be regarded as the true OR gate action, but in practice it tends to be less useful than the conventional OR gate action, and exclusive

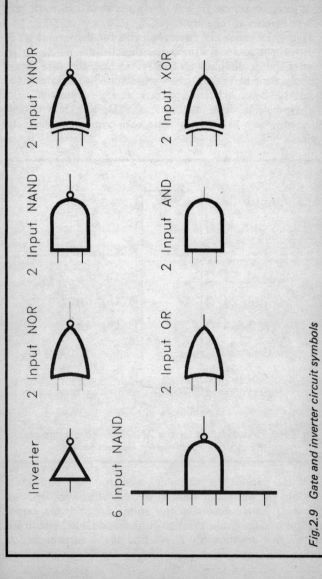

Fig.2.9 Gate and inverter circuit symbols

OR gates are something of a rarity. There are also exclusive NOR gates, and these are effectively just an exclusive OR gate with an inverter at the output.

Figure 2.9 shows the circuit symbols for the various types of two input gate. It also shows the circuit symbols for an inverter and a multi-input (NAND) gate. Note that gate circuit symbols seem to be less rigidly standardised than most other circuit symbols, and that you may well encounter different gate symbols in other publications. However, it is usually fairly obvious what type of gate each symbol is meant to depict.

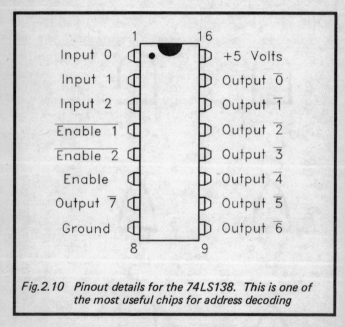

Fig.2.10   Pinout details for the 74LS138. This is one of the most useful chips for address decoding

Of the various decoder chips available the 74LS138 is probably the most useful low cost type for address decoding purposes. Pinout details for this 16 pin d.i.l. chip are shown in Figure 2.10. It is a three to eight line decoder, and it has outputs that are normally high. One of the outputs goes to the low state, and which output this is depends on the binary code on the inputs. This table shows which set of input states activates each output.

INPUT 0	INPUT 1	INPUT 2	OUTPUT
Low	Low	Low	0
Low	Low	High	1
Low	High	Low	2
Low	High	High	3
High	Low	Low	4
High	Low	High	5
High	High	Low	6
High	High	High	7

The 74LS138 is rather more useful than it might at first appear. The first point to note is that there are three further inputs. In most cases it is not limited to decoding three lines, and can actually decode up to six lines. The additional three lines are "enable" types, and unless they are taken to the appropriate state, the outputs of the device all go to the third logic state. In other words they simply go to a high impedance state, and will not drive logic inputs. The inputs at pins 4 and 5 are negative enable inputs, and they must be taken to logic 0 in order to make the device function normally. The enable input at pin 6 is a positive type, and this pin must be taken high in order to produce normal operation of the chip.

The second point to note is that different sets of input states activate different outputs of the 74LS138. This gives the potential of having the device decode several blocks of addresses, with each block having its own output. Even if you do not require several decoded outputs on one card, it is possible to standardise on the same decoder circuit for several cards, with a different output being used on each card. You could, for example, have the &H300 to &H31F address range split into four blocks of eight addresses, with each block activating a different output of the 74LS138. You could then have up to four do-it-yourself expansion cards using the same basic address decoder circuit, provided each card utilized a different output of its address decoder.

It is perhaps worth mentioning that there is a very similar device to the 74LS138, the 74LS137. This only differs from the 74LS138 in that the activated output goes high, and all the others are low. If you require an address decoder which provides a high pulse when activated, then using a 74LS137 instead of a 74LS138 should provide the desired circuit action. In practice it almost invariably seems to be a low pulse that is required in order to drive computer peripheral chips, and so we will be using the 74LS138 in the decoder circuits described here.

Decoder Circuits
A popular method of PC address decoding is to have a decoder circuit based on a 74LS30 eight input NAND gate. This has an output which goes low if all eight inputs are high, or high if any of the inputs are low. Obviously you will not need a PC address decoder that decodes eight lines to the high state. Typically the requirement is for something more like a decoder which is activated by four lines high and four lines low. The simple way around this problem is to feed to the 74LS30 via inverters any lines that must be decoded to the low state.

Figure 2.11 shows a typical address decoder based on a 74LS30 eight input NAND gate plus some inverters. In this case there are four inverters, and these are part of a 74LS14 hex Schmitt trigger/inverter package. However, this general scheme of things should work properly using any 74LS** series inverters. This decoder is designed to act as a "Write" decoder. It decodes A4, A8, and A9 to the high state, and A5 to A7 to the low state. This means that it will be activated when any address from &H310 to &H31F is accessed for a write operation. If A4 was to be fed to IC2 via an inverter, it would then be decoded to the low state, and the circuit would be activated by write operations to addresses from &H300 to &H30F. Connect −IOR instead of −IOW, and the decoder will then act as a read type.

This type of address decoder is very cheap and simple, but as pointed out previously, it can be a bit awkward when it comes to actually building the circuit. It is also slightly lacking in versatility. Figure 2.12 shows the circuit diagram

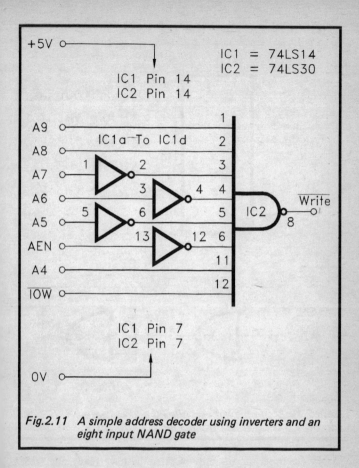

Fig.2.11 A simple address decoder using inverters and an eight input NAND gate

for a PC address decoder based on a 74LS138. This is still pretty cheap and simple, but it is much more versatile than the circuit based on the 74LS30.

A minimalist PC address decoder would have to decode address lines from A5 to A9, plus AEN and possibly −IOR or −IOW. It is just possible to do this using a 74LS138, with the only proviso that any decoding of −IOR or −IOW must be provided separately. Figure 2.13 shows the circuit for a minimalist address decoder of this type, and I suppose this

47

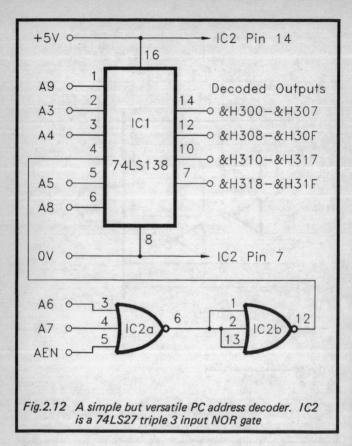

Fig.2.12 A simple but versatile PC address decoder. IC2 is a 74LS27 triple 3 input NOR gate

could be used if you only wanted to have (say) one 8255 parallel interface chip in the &H300 to &H31F address space. However, by using a very simple address decoder of this type you would be painting yourself into the proverbial corner, and it would be difficult to add more user add-ons at a later date.

The circuit of Figure 2.12 offers much greater versatility, but it requires the use of an extra chip. This is a 74LS27 triple three input NOR gate. In this circuit only two of the gates are required, and no connections are made to the third

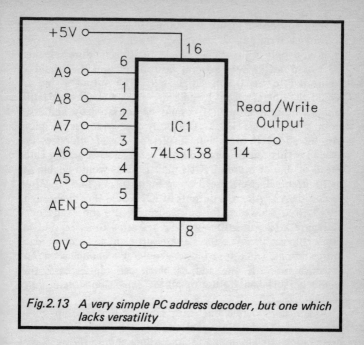

Fig.2.13 *A very simple PC address decoder, but one which lacks versatility*

gate. IC2b is simply wired as an inverter, and it effectively converts IC2a into a three input OR gate. It might seem to be easier to simply use a three input OR gate, but a suitable device seems to be difficult to obtain. The 74LS27 is widely available, and is easily wired to give the required circuit action.

This arrangement enables three lines to drive one input of the 74LS138, permitting a maximum of eight rather than six lines to be decoded. A6, A7, and AEN are decoded to the low state by the gates and one of the low enable inputs of IC1. The other low enable input decodes A5, while the high enable input decodes A8. A9 is fed to input 0, and it is effectively decoded to the high state. This renders four of IC1's eight outputs effectively inoperative. Inputs 1 and 2 of IC1 decode A3 and A4, and the states on these lines, when all the other decoded lines are at the appropriate logic levels, dictates which of the four outputs of IC1 is activated. In other words, the &H300 to &H31F address range is divided into four blocks of eight addresses. Figure 2.12 shows which range of addresses activate each output.

If you only wanted two blocks of sixteen addresses, then A3 would not be decoded, and instead, pin 2 of IC1 would be connected to the 0 volt supply rail. The output at pin 14 would then be activated by addresses from &H300 to &H30F, and the output at pin 10 would be activated by addresses from &H310 to &H31F. Obviously more address decoding can be added if more but smaller blocks of addresses are needed. This can be accomplished using another gate or gates ahead of one or more of IC1's inputs. This would enable A9 to be decoded elsewhere, leaving input 0 (pin 1) of IC1 free to decode A2. All eight outputs of IC1 would then be brought into action. However, for most purposes the address decoder of Figure 2.12 will suffice without resorting to any modifications. Blocks of eight addresses are sufficient to accommodate most add-ons, while four blocks should give enough scope for expansion. With one address block per add-on card, this would be sufficient to use up all the expansion slots in most computers.

As already pointed out, with some peripheral chips there is no need to bother about decoding −IOW and −IOR, since some chips provide inputs for these lines and do the necessary decoding. This is not always the case though, and when using circuits that are wholly or largely based on TTL logic chips, you will normally have to decode −IOR and −IOW. Figure 2.14 shows a simple PC address decoder and the additional circuitry needed in order to produce separate read and write output signals. This basically just consists of processing the −IOW line and the output of the decoder using a two input OR gate. During a write operation to the appropriate address range, both of these lines will go low, and so will the output of the gate. Essentially the same system is used with a second OR gate to process the −IOR line and produce a read output. A negative chip select output is still available from the basic address decoder circuit, and can be used with any chips that have built-in processing for −IOW and −IOR. Note that this method of gating should work perfectly well with any address decoder circuit, but only if it provides negative output pulses.

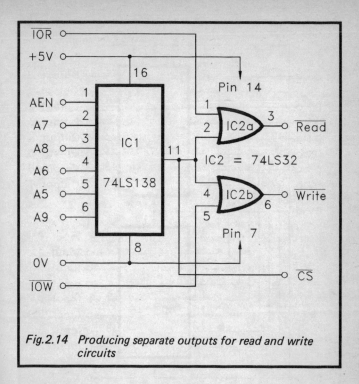

Fig.2.14 Producing separate outputs for read and write circuits

Parallel I/O Ports

In order to produce an eight bit output port all that is needed is an address decoder plus an eight bit latch. Simply using something like a tristate eight bit buffer to provide an output port is not usually acceptable. This would only provide a valid output for the duration that the data bus was fed through to the outputs. This is likely to be well under a microsecond in practice. What is needed is a circuit that will latch this momentary flash of data, so that the outputs can be used to drive relays, l.e.d.s, digital to analogue converters, or whatever. The situation is generally somewhat different when it comes to inputting data. You normally have a set of what are essentially static input levels, and these must be fed through to the data bus while the port is

51

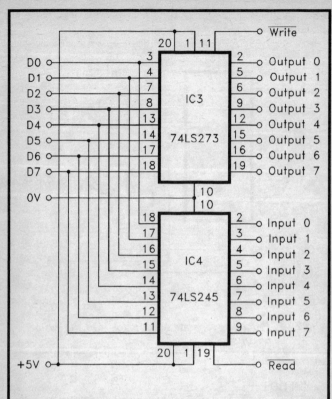

Fig.2.15 A simple 8 bit PC input/output port. Note that this requires an address decoder circuit in order to function properly

read. An eight bit tristate buffer is all that is needed to achieve this.

Figure 2.15 shows the circuit diagram for a basic PC eight bit input/output port. This is basically the same sort of circuit that has been used with numerous eight bit home computers over the years, and it seems to work reliably with most PCs. Note that this circuit must be used in conjunction with a suitable address decoder circuit. This must be a decoder which includes the extra decoding to provide separate read and write outputs.

It is also worth noting that although no supply decoupling capacitors are featured in any of the circuits in this book, these must be included on any PC expansion cards. These are merely ceramic capacitors of about 100 nanofarads in value connected across the supply lines. Some circuit designers use one capacitor per TTL integrated circuit, with each capacitor mounted as close as possible to its respective integrated circuit. However, this is probably using a certain amount of over-kill, and one decoupling capacitor per three TTL integrated circuits (or other logic chips) should suffice.

The eight bit output port of Figure 2.15 is provided by a 74LS273 octal D type flip/flop. The data bus connects to its D (data) inputs, and the latching output lines are provided by the Q outputs. These are non-inverting outputs which latch at whatever states are present on the D inputs when there is a positive transition on the CP (clock pulse) input. This transition is, of course, provided by the trailing edge of the write pulse from the address decoder.

The input port is provided by a 74LS245 octal transceiver (IC4). Conventionally an octal tristate buffer such as a 74LS244 is used in applications of this type. I prefer to use the 74LS245 simply because its pinout arrangement is a more convenient one which helps to keep board layouts more simple and straightforward. In this case IC4 has pin 1 wired to the +5 volt supply so that it is permanently in the "send" mode. Its tristate outputs are controlled by the negative chip enable input at pin 19. When a negative pulse is received from the read output of the address decoder, the outputs are activated and the eight bit input code is fed through to the PC's data bus.

The 8255

The standard parallel interface chip for the PCs (and many other computers come to that) is the 8255. This is bus compatible with the 8080 and 8086 series of microprocessors, and with the Z80 series. The Z80A microprocessor has been used in several popular eight bit home computers, and the 8255 was popular in user add-ons for these machines. This chip may well be familiar to many readers, but it will be described in reasonable detail for the benefit of those who have not encountered it previously.

It is a 40 pin d.i.l. chip which provides three eight bit input/output ports. This is one eight bit port more than many parallel interface adaptor chips, such as the 6522 and 6821. However, it is not quite as good as it may at first appear. Whereas chips such as the 6522 only provide two eight bit ports, they also provide two handshake lines per port. These handshake lines are sufficiently versatile to accommodate any normal handshaking arrangements. This enables the two eight bit ports to operate properly in any normal situations, including those where controlling the flow of data into or out of the port is critical and difficult.

By contrast, the ports of the 8255 have no handshake lines at all. Instead, where handshaking is needed, port C is split into two four bit ports. One nibble is set as outputs while the other nibble is set as inputs, and these act as the handshake lines for Ports A and B. Thus, if you need eight bit ports plus handshake lines, you only have two ports, plus (probably) a few left-over input and output lines from port C. If you require just basic input or output ports with no handshaking, then the 8255 has more to offer than most other parallel interface adaptors. On the other hand, if you do require handshaking it has little advantage. Although it might provide a few spare lines on port C, it is probably slightly less convenient to use than most other parallel port chips.

It is only fair to point out another relative shortcoming of the 8255, which is a lack of individual control over the functions of its input/output lines. With devices such as the 6522 and 6821 there is a data direction register for each port. By way of this register it is possible to set each line as an input or an output, as desired. If you require a port to have five lines as outputs to control relay drivers, and three as inputs to read sensor switches, then this is perfectly possible. You have full control over which lines are used as the inputs and which are set as the outputs. With the 8255 all eight lines of a port must be set as outputs, or all eight must be set as inputs. The only exception to this is port C. As explained previously, this can be set for simple split operation (four lines as inputs and

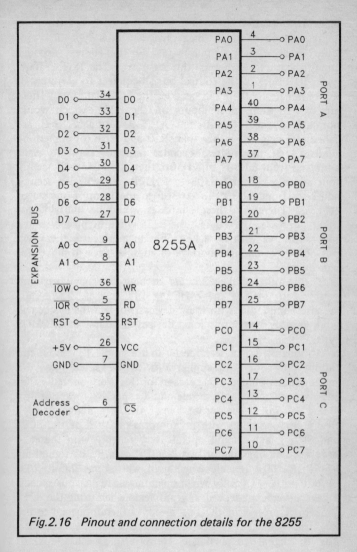

Fig.2.16 Pinout and connection details for the 8255

four lines as outputs).

Figure 2.16 gives pinout details for the 8255, and it also shows the correct method of connecting it to the PC expansion bus. The negative chip select input (pin 6) is fed from the address decoder, which must obviously be a type that provides negative output pulses (as do the address decoder circuits featured earlier in this chapter). The RST, —IOW, and —IOR lines of the control bus all connect to corresponding terminals of the 8255, as does the 8 bit data bus. There are two register select inputs on the 8255, which would normally connect to A0 and A1. Accordingly, they are called A0 and A1 rather than RS0 and RS1 (or something similar). If the address decoder responds (say) to eight addresses from &H309 to &H30F, then the 8255 will occupy four addresses from &H308 to &H30B. It will also occupy addresses from &H30C to &H30F in the form of one set of echoes. Therefore, these addresses would be unusable for other purposes. Of course, the 8255 could be placed in just four addresses with no echoes, but in most cases there will not be a great enough shortage of address space to make this worthwhile.

The outputs of the 8255 are latching types, and are compatible with 74LS** and 74HCT** TTL devices. The inputs are also compatible with these devices. In fact the device will work reliably with most logic devices, including most CMOS types.

Although it might seem better to use simple TTL input and output ports for most applications, the 8255 tends to be a more popular choice. One reason for this is undoubtedly that it provides a reasonably simple and inexpensive means of providing a lot of input/output lines. Also, it is designed specifically for operation with microprocessors such as the 8088 and 80286, and should operate very reliably with these. I have encountered one or two PCs that seem to be something less than 100% reliable when used with some simple TTL output ports, especially when operating at higher bus speeds. I have never experienced any problems when using the 8255 though, regardless of the bus speed. I therefore tend to use it as my standard method of interfacing the PC expansion bus to digital to analogue converters, speech chips, or whatever.

8255 Programming

There is insufficient space available here to go into great detail about all the 8255 operating modes, and methods of using this device. Anyone using practically any computer peripheral chip would be well advised to obtain the relevant data sheet, and I would certainly recommend this for anyone who is going to use a chip as complex as the 8255. However, here we will consider the basic ways of using this interface chip, which should at least get you started, and may be all that you need in order to use the chip effectively in your particular applications.

The 8255 has four read/write registers. Three of these are ports A, B, and C. Obviously each one of these would normally be used only as a read register or a write type, depending on whether its port has been set as an input or an output type. The exception to this is when port C is used in the split mode of operation, and it is then a form of read/write register. The fourth register is a control type, and data would normally only be written to this. You can read data from this register, but it will not furnish anything meaningful. If you need a record of what has been written to the control register, a byte of RAM must be used to store a copy of each control number that is written to this register. If we assume that the 8255 is at the example address range mentioned earlier (&H308 to &H30B), then the base addresses of the four registers would be as follows:

HEX ADDRESS	DEC. ADDRESS	REGISTER
&H308	776	Port A
&H309	777	Port B
&H30A	778	Port C
&H30B	779	Control

Using the ports is straightforward enough, but the control register is a bit tricky to fully master, Figure 2.17 helps illustrate its use. There are three modes of operation for the 8255, which have been designated modes 0, 1, and 2. Mode 0 is the most simple, and is the one you should use when initially experimenting with the 8255. In this mode the ports operate as simple input/output types, with the only complication that port C can operate in the split mode (one nibble

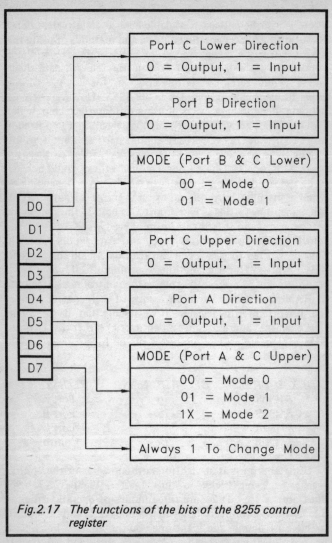

Fig.2.17 The functions of the bits of the 8255 control register

as inputs and the other nibble as outputs).

The required operating mode is set by bits five to seven of the control register. Bit seven is set high in order to enable the operating mode to be changed. Be careful to set this bit high, as the control register operates in a totally different manner if this bit is set to zero. Bits five and six control the operating mode. This table shows how this scheme of things operates.

MODE	BIT 7	BIT 6	BIT 5
0	1	0	0
1	1	0	1
2	1	1	0
2	1	1	1

As will be apparent from this table, there are two control codes which select mode 2. It does not matter which one you use, the effect on the 8255 is exactly the same. These bits only control the mode of port A and the upper nibble of port C. Port B and the lower nibble of port C are controlled by bit 2 of the control register. This is either high for mode 1 operation, or low if you require mode 0 operation. Mode 2 is not applicable to these ports, and so one bit is all that is needed for their mode control.

Bits zero, one, three, and four are used to control the functions of the ports (i.e. whether they operate as inputs or outputs). This operates in the following manner.

PORT	CONTROL BIT	DEC. VALUE WHEN HIGH
0	C Lower	1
1	B	2
3	C Upper	8
4	A	16

In order to set a port as an output type the control bit is set to zero. Setting a control bit to 1 obviously sets its respective port as an input type. Those who are used to the 6522, 6821, etc., should note that this works the opposite way round to the data direction registers of these chips.

When writing to the control register you must set the mode of operation and the port directions in a single write operation. You can not write to bits five to seven first, and then bits zero, one, three, and four. However, working out the right control register values is not difficult. For mode 0 operation bits five and six are low, and bit seven is high. To set bit seven high a decimal value of 128 is required. The table provided previously shows the decimal value needed for each control bit when it is set high (i.e. when its port is to be set as an input). A value of zero is, of course, needed for any bits that will be set low.

Simply take the values given in the table for the ports that are to be set as inputs, and add 128 to the total of these values. You then have the value to write to the control register. For example, assume that port A and both nibbles of port C are to be set as inputs. The values for these ports as inputs are sixteen, eight, and one. This gives a total of twenty-five. Adding 128 to this gives a grand total of 153, which is the value that must be written to the control register. In GW BASIC, and using the example port addresses mentioned previously, this value would be written to the control register using the instruction:

OUT 779,153

You can use hexadecimal addresses with GW BASIC if you prefer, but remember that hexadecimal numbers are indicated using the "&H" prefix, not just the "&" prefix used in some languages. Numbers having just the "&" prefix may well be accepted, as I think that these are interpreted by GW BASIC as octal (base eight) numbers. This has led me into some time consuming errors in the past as I tend to use just the "&" prefix from force of habit (having mainly used a BBC computer for interfacing in the past). Consequently, I now always use decimal input/output addresses when using GW BASIC.

For many purposes mode 0 operation will suffice. For example, there are many applications which do not require any form of handshaking. These include such things as driving digital to analogue converters, relay drivers, etc., and reading simple sensors. For applications of this type you only need simple input and output lines, and there is no point in using anything beyond mode 0. Where handshaking is needed, setting port C for split operation to provide the handshake input/output lines will often suffice. This does not provide edge triggered inputs or anything of this type, but simple input and output lines will usually be sufficient. Remember that where necessary you can always use some external signal processing, such as a pulse stretcher or shortener, in order to make things more reliable. For instance, if an output is providing very brief pulses, a pulse stretcher might provide a signal which can be read more reliably, with no pulses passing undetected by the handshake input.

Where complex handshaking is needed it might be better to resort to mode 1 operation. This uses port A and port B as eight bit input/output ports, and six lines of port C to act as strobed handshake lines and interrupt control signals (three lines per port). Mode 2 provides strobed bidirectional operation through port A, with five lines of port C acting as what I suppose is a sort of control bus. This is not a mode that I have ever used, and it is presumably only needed for a few specialised applications. Anyway, to fully get to grips with the 8255 you really need to study the data sheet and then experiment a little.

Other 82** series devices interface to the PC buses in much the same way as the 8255. Devices that are bus compatible with the 82** series of peripheral chips should also interface to the PC expansion bus without difficulty. It is often possible to interface peripheral chips for one series of microprocessors to a microprocessor from a different range. For example, chips intended for the 6502 and similar microprocessors have been used successfully with the Z80 microprocessor. It is usually possible to overcome the differences between the control buses, but it can take a certain amount of experimentation to get things right. For example, where a peripheral chip has a combined read/write line, either −IOW or −IOR might provide a suitable signal. If not, then inverting one of these lines or feeding it through a monostable might produce the desired result. If a negative reset signal is needed, then feeding the PC's reset line via an inverter should give the desired result, or you can put a suitable reset generator circuit on the expansion card. Studying the timing diagrams in data sheets can steer you in the right direction, but in the end it comes down to the "suck it and see" approach.

Design Examples

Bear in mind that devices which are described as "microprocessor bus compatible", or something similar, might not be compatible with the PC's version of a microprocessor bus. While most microprocessor compatible devices can probably be interfaced direct to the PC buses successfully, this may not always be feasible. With some peripheral chips it is probably best not to attempt to interface them direct onto the PC expansion bus. With a device such as the Ferranti ZN426E digital to analogue converter for example, it is generally easier to drive it from a simple eight bit output port (such as a port of an 8255) than to connect it direct onto the data bus. In fact with devices such as this there is usually no option but to use an 8 bit latching port, since there are no built-in latches. With some analogue to digital converters, such as the popular Ferranti ZN447E series, direct interfacing of a sort is usually possible, but it can sometimes be easier to interface them via an eight bit input (which will need to be augmented by one or two handshake lines).

On the other hand, the ADC08** series of analogue/digital devices are designed to interface on to PC type buses, and should do so without difficulty. You have to carefully assess each interfacing problem, and work out the most appropriate solution. When in doubt it is probably best to take the safer but more complex approach, and interface to the PC expansion bus indirectly via an 8255 (or whatever).

We will now consider some examples of interfacing devices to the PC bus, in order to illustrate the problems that can arise and some possible solutions to them. We will use analogue to digital and digital to analogue converters as our design examples as these are fairly typical in the interfacing problems they provide. The circuits described can actually be used as the basis of your own projects, as we will be dealing with practical integrated circuits, not notional devices. The circuits have all been tried and tested.

Some devices are much easier to interface to the PC expansion bus than others, and the ZN426E and ADC0844

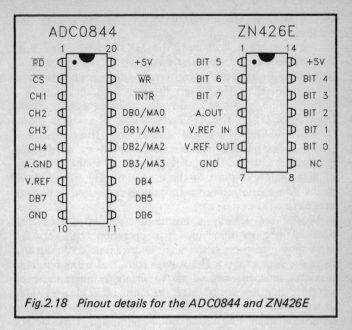

Fig.2.18 Pinout details for the ADC0844 and ZN426E

respectively represent the difficult and the easy. Pinout details for these devices are shown in Figure 2.18. The problem with the ZN426E is that it is not a microprocessor compatible device. The ADC0844 on the other hand, is designed specifically to interface to 8080 and 8088 type buses. We will consider the ADC0844 first.

This analogue to digital converter chip has an eight bit data bus (DB0 to DB7) with tristate outputs. It can therefore output to the data bus by driving the chip select (−CS) input from a suitable address decoder circuit. There is no need for the address decoder to process −IOR or −IOW as there are inputs for these on the ADC0844 (−RD and −WR).

You will notice from Figure 2.18 that the lower four bits of the address bus are labelled DB0/MA0 to DB3/MA3. This is due to the fact that these pins are dual purpose, and also operate as what the ADC0844 data sheet refers to as address inputs. This is perhaps not a strictly accurate way of looking at things since the chip only occupies a single address, and these pins do slightly more than switch between several internal registers.

The basic method of using the ADC0844 is to first write to the device in order to start a conversion, and to then read it in order to extract the converted value. Sometimes with this type of thing the value written to the chip is simply a dummy value, and can be any legal value (i.e. any integer from 0 to 255). The ADC0844 is a fairly complex device though, and it has four analogue inputs. There is actually only one converter, but this is preceded by a four-way multiplexer (an electronic switch) that can connect any one of these inputs through to the converter. The value written to the device determines which input is connected through to the converter.

Matters are actually a bit more complicated than this, because there are three modes of operation available. The most simple of these is the single-ended mode, and with this there are four inputs. The voltage converted is the potential from the analogue ground pin to whichever input has been selected. In other words, this is the normal four channel mode of the device. You will notice from Figure 2.18 that there are separate analogue and digital ground terminals. These do not necessarily have to be held at the same potential, but in most cases they would simply be wired together and connected to a common analogue/digital ground.

There are two differential modes available, and in the standard differential mode there are two inputs available. The first uses what would normally be the channel 1 and channel 2 inputs, while the second uses the channel 3 and channel 4 inputs. The other differential mode is a pseudo type, in which the channel 4 input acts as a common negative input, and the other three inputs respond to their voltage relative to the channel 4 input. In other words, if you wish to measure voltages with respect to a potential other than the earth one, connect the channel 4 input to a suitable offset voltage, and then use inputs 1 to 3 to measure the voltages. Note that in the differential and pseudo differential modes the analogue ground terminal is not used as an input, but it would normally be connected to ground anyway. Figure 2.19 shows the avail-

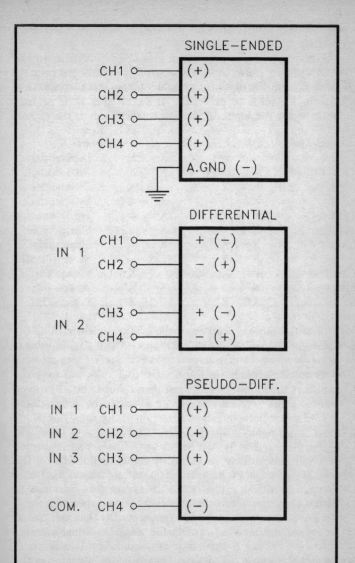

Fig.2.19   The input arrangements for the three modes of
            the ADC0844

able modes in diagrammatic form, and might help to clarify matters.

This table shows the values that must be written to the ADC0844 in order to select each of the available operating modes, and the options available within each mode (e.g. which channel is to be read). The table shows the polarity with which the input signals must be applied to the device.

CONTROL	CH1	CH2	CH3	CH4	A.GND	MODE
0	+	−	X	X	X	Differential
1	−	+	X	X	X	Differential
2	X	X	+	−	X	Differential
3	X	X	−	+	X	Differential
4	+	X	X	X	−	Single-ended
5	X	+	X	X	−	Single-ended
6	X	X	+	X	−	Single-ended
7	X	X	X	+	−	Single-ended
12	+	X	X	−	X	Pseudo Diff.
13	X	+	X	−	X	Pseudo Diff.
14	X	X	+	−	X	Pseudo Diff.

The full range sensitivity of the device is controlled by the reference voltage fed to the V.REF pin. The full range value is achieved at whatever voltage is used as the reference potential. This voltage must be in the range 0 to 5 volts, but for good results it should not be much less than about 1 volt. For some purposes the reference voltage can simply be provided by the +5 volt supply, or can be a fraction of this supply obtained via a simple potential divider.

Neither method is particularly satisfactory because the +5 volt rail is not likely to be highly stable or noise-free. The stability of most PC +5 volt rails is not actually all that bad, but for a critical application such as using an analogue to digital converter for accurate measurements, very well stabilised reference voltages are often needed. One method of using the device which avoids the need for a highly stable reference voltage is the ratiometric method. This is where the input voltages are derived from potential dividers across the +5 volt supply, as in Figure 2.20. Although the potentiometers are shown as being presets in Figure 2.20, in reality

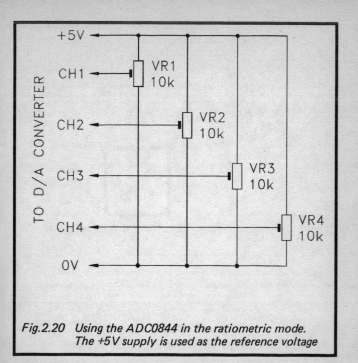

*Fig.2.20   Using the ADC0844 in the ratiometric mode.
The +5V supply is used as the reference voltage*

they could be ordinary potentiometers, or even potential dividers having a fixed resistor for one element, and a thermistor or some other type of sensor as the other element. The +5 volt rail is used as the reference voltage. The point about this method is that any change in the supply voltage will affect both the reference potential and the input potential. The two changes cancel out one another, giving no change in readings.

Where a highly stable reference voltage is needed, any of the many low voltage reference generator chips should be suitable. Figure 2.21 shows a simple 1.2 volt regulator circuit based on the 8069 voltage regulator or an equivalent device. This gives a highly stabilised reference voltage which has excellent temperature stability.

The −INTR pin is a status output. The conversion process is not an instant process, or even a particularly fast one. The

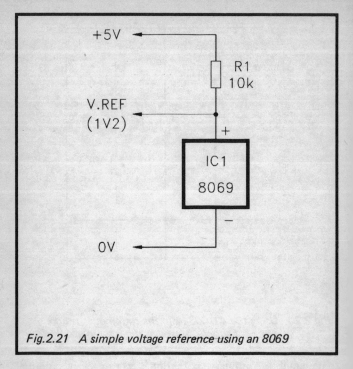

Fig.2.21   A simple voltage reference using an 8069

ADC0844 is fairly average in terms of its conversion time, which is typically about 30 µs at 25 degrees Centigrade. Obviously data must not be read from the device prematurely, as invalid data would then be obtained. One method of avoiding this problem, and one which usually works well in practice, is to simply have a timing loop to provide a delay between issuing each start conversion signal and reading the converter. If necessary, some experimentation can be used in order to find the optimum delay time (i.e. the shortest delay which gives reliable operation).   Bear in mind that if you are using a fairly slow computer language, such as an interpreted BASIC, you may well find that you can not read the device prematurely. No time delay loop will then be needed. Using GW BASIC on a 10 MHz "turbo" XT type PC I found that no time delay was needed.

An alternative to using a time delay is to have an input line to read the −INTR output. This is normally high, and goes low when a conversion has been completed. The hold-off would then be obtained by monitoring −INTR using a simple loop routine, and only permitting the converter to be read once −INTR had gone low. Incidentally, −INTR is reset automatically when the converter is read.

There is a slight problem with this method in that an input line is required. If the analogue to digital converter is part of a large interface card, then there may well be a spare input somewhere that can be used. However, if it is on a simple ADC card, there will probably be no spare lines that can be used. Clearly, adding an 8255 in order to read one line would be using the proverbial "sledgehammer to crack a nut", and using a 74LS245 to provide one line would not be much better. A more practical approach is to use a device such as the 74LS125 which can provide up to four input lines. Figure 2.22 shows how this device can be used as a quad input port. Of course, if you only need one input line, you can use one of the buffers and ignore the other three. However, it is not a bad idea to implement all four lines, since the spare inputs might turn out to be useful for something.

There is a third option, which is to use the −INTR output to generate an interrupt. This is not difficult from the hardware point of view, but you need to be fairly expert at PC programming in order to handle this type of thing. In an application of this type it is not normally necessary to resort to using interrupts. It is only likely to be worthwhile doing so in applications that are processor intensive, and where it would therefore be unacceptable to have the processor idling away waiting for conversions to be completed. Few applications for analogue to digital converters fall into this category. Mostly a set of readings are read and stored in memory, and they are only processed once a full set has be gathered, and no more readings will be taken. In some cases readings are taken and immediately displayed on the screen, which is not usually very demanding on the microprocessor.

Figure 2.23 shows the circuit diagram for an analogue to digital converter based on the ADC0844, complete with details of the connections to the PC expansion bus. This

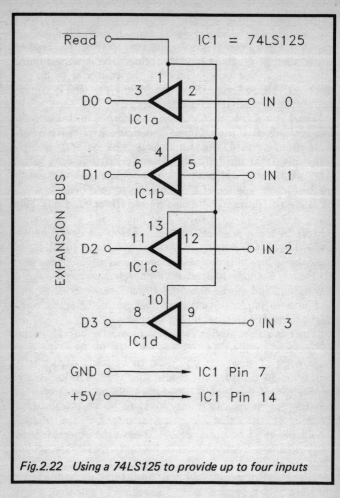

Fig.2.22   Using a 74LS125 to provide up to four inputs

circuit uses the +5 volt supply as the reference voltage. Remember that the address decoder should be a type which does not decode −IOR and −IOW, as these are dealt with by the ADC0844. This circuit does not utilize the −INTR status output, and my preference is to simply use a delay loop if there is a danger of taking readings too frequently.

70

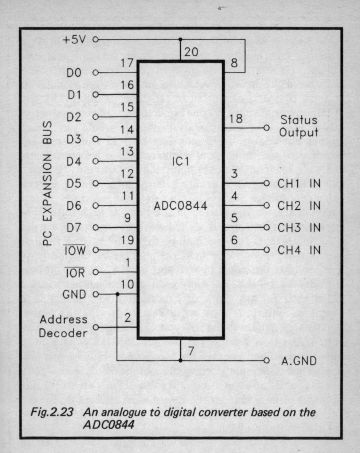

Fig.2.23 An analogue to digital converter based on the ADC0844

One final point is that the ADC0844 usually has a suffix to the basic type number. The suffix indicates the case style and operating temperature range of the component. You are most likely to see the ADC0844CCN advertised in component catalogues, and this is the version I use. Any version of the device should be satisfactory for normal purposes though.

Digital to Analogue

The ZN426E provides the opposite function to the ADC0844 — it converts a digital value into a corresponding analogue

71

voltage. The ZN426E is a fairly simple converter, but it does have the refinement of an on-chip reference voltage generator. This is a high quality type which gives a 2.55 volt reference voltage. This is a convenient figure as it represents 10 millivolts per digit. In other words, the output voltage in millivolts is equal to the value written to the device multiplied by ten. Alternatively, dividing by one hundred gives the output potential in volts. For example, a value of 123 would produce an output potential of 1230 millivolts, or 1.23 volts. It is not essential to use the integral reference voltage generator, since there are separate reference input and output pins. However, in practice there will normally be no point in using a separate reference voltage source. If an external reference voltage should be used, it must be in the range 0 to 3 volts. For optimum performance it should be between 2 and 3 volts.

The ZN426E has no built-in data latches, and its data inputs must therefore be fed from an 8 bit latching port. In a PC context this could be one port of an 8255, or eight lines provided by a 74LS273. Only eight lines are needed, as there is no need for any form of handshaking with a digital to analogue converter. You write data to it, and the output adjusts very rapidly to the new voltage. In reality the response time is less than instant, but the ZN426E can handle up to about one million conversions per second. In most practical applications the computer would not be in danger of outputting values at a higher rate than this. In any event, the rate at which data is sent to the device must be kept down to a suitable level by software routines, as there is no hardware solution to this problem.

Figure 2.24 shows the circuit diagram for a digital to analogue converter based on the ZN426E. The main point to note here is that the internal reference voltage source requires a discrete load resistor (R1) and decoupling capacitor (C1). The source impedance of the output voltage is about 10k, which means that in most practical applications it will need to be buffered using an operational amplifier. In fact in most applications the output will need a certain amount of amplification anyway.

A device such as the ZN426E is probably only a worthwhile prospect in a PC add-on if it is part of a large interface

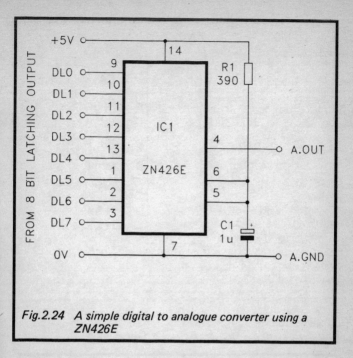

Fig.2.24 A simple digital to analogue converter using a ZN426E

board which has a spare eight bit output. Where no such port is available, it is probably better to use a PC bus compatible device. The ZN428E is a suitable device, and although this is not designed specifically for an 8080/8088 type bus, it will readily interface to the PC expansion bus. In fact the ZN428E will readily interface to practically any microprocessor buses. This device has the pinout arrangement shown in Figure 2.25, and it is basically just a ZN426E with an eight bit data latch added at the input. Interfacing this device straight onto the PC expansion bus is therefore quite straightforward. It might actually be cheaper to use a ZN426E plus an external data latch such as a 74LS273, but the convenience of the ZN428E is probably well worth the additional cost.

Interfacing the ZN428E onto the PC expansion bus is very much like using an 8 bit data latch. You simply connect its data bus and supply lines to the corresponding PC bus lines,

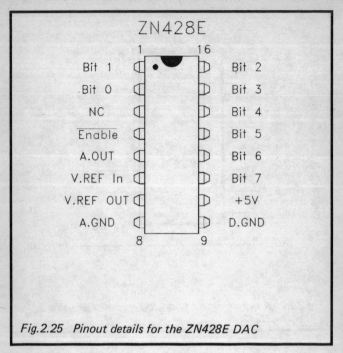

Fig.2.25 Pinout details for the ZN428E DAC

and drive the negative enable input from the write output of an address decoder. Figure 2.26 shows the circuit diagram for a digital to analogue converter based on the ZN428E. Like the ZN426E, a load resistor (R1) and decoupling capacitor (C1) are needed for its internal 2.55 volt reference generator.

The ZN448E ADC

There is a sort of complementary chip to the ZN428E in the form of the ZN427E analogue to digital converter. These days the ZN448E tends to be more popular, and this is basically just a ZN427E having a built-in clock oscillator. There are actually three devices in the ZN448E series, which are the ZN447E, the ZN448E, and the ZN449E. They are esentially the same device, and differ only in their guaranteed accuracies. These are respectively: 0.25 LSB, 0.5 LSB, and 1 LSB. The

74

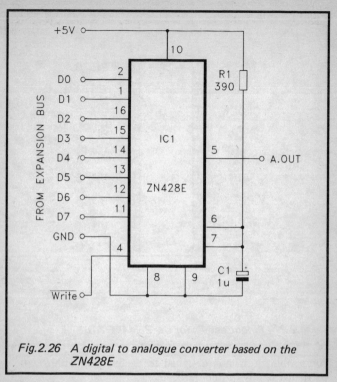

Fig.2.26 A digital to analogue converter based on the ZN428E

ZN448E is the most popular of this series, as it offers a good compromise between accuracy and cost. It is the only version of the device offered by many component suppliers. Pinout details for the ZN448E series of chips are provided in Figure 2.27.

In common with the other Ferranti ADC/DAC chips mentioned in this book, the ZN448E has a built-in 2.55 volt reference voltage generator, plus the option of using an external reference if desired. It has an eight bit data bus with tristate outputs. This can therefore interface direct onto the data buses of a microprocessor. The device has read (−RD) and write (−WR) inputs, but these are not compatible with the read and write lines of the PC expansion bus. Although the ZN448E is designed to be microprocessor bus

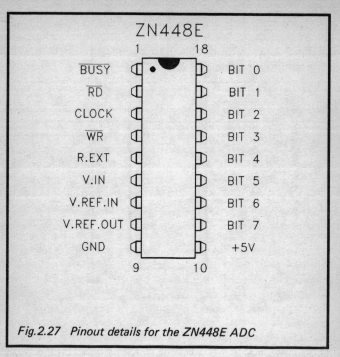

Fig.2.27   Pinout details for the ZN448E ADC

compatible, it is not designed to be bus compatible with a
particular family of microprocessors.

The write input must be driven from the write output of
an address decoder circuit. All this actually does is to start a
conversion. The value written to the converter is simply a
dummy value which will be ignored by the ZN448E (its data
bus is a set of outputs, not a bidirectional type). The read line
must be fed from the read output of an address decoder. This
activates the tristate buffers and takes a reading from the
device. There is a status output in the form of the –BUSY
line. As its name implies, this terminal goes low while a
conversion is in progress. A hold-off to prevent premature
readings being taken can be provided by monitoring this
output until it goes high. Like the ADC0844 described
previously, this requires an input line to be provided by one
section of a 74LS125, or whatever. In practice it is usually

76

easier to simply ignore the status output and use a timing loop to provide the hold-off.

Pin 3 is the clock input, and a capacitor connected between this terminal and ground sets the clock frequency. The clock frequency can be up to 1 MHz, and a conversion takes nine clock cycles. This represents a conversion time of 9 μs, or a maximum of over 100,000 conversions per second, which is pretty good for a successive approximation converter. A "tail" resistor connects to pin 5 (R.EXT). This is part of the high speed comparator which compares the input voltage to internally generated reference levels. The other end of the tail resistor must go to a negative supply, and the -5 volt supply of the PC expansion bus is suitable for this purpose.

Figure 2.28 shows the circuit diagram for an analogue to digital converter based on the ZN448E. R2 and C1 are the load resistor and decoupling capacitor for the internal precision 2.55 volt reference generator. With a full scale sensitivity of 2.55 volts and eight bit resolution, the resolution in voltage terms is 10 millivolts (0.01 volts). To convert readings into an input voltage simply divide by one hundred. R1 is the "tail" resistor, and a value of 82k is apposite for a negative supply rail of -5 volts. The current drawn from the negative supply rail is only about 60 microamps, so there is no risk of overloading the -5 volt rail! The ZN448E seems to be largely immune to noise or instability on the negative supply rail incidentally. If your PC's -5 volt rail is not particularly well smoothed or stabilised, this should not affect the performance of this converter.

C2 is the capacitor which sets the clock frequency. This sets the operating frequency at roughly the maximum figure of 1 MHz. It is worth noting that the ZN448E is guaranteed to operate up to at least 1 MHz, and that most of these devices will in fact operate quite happily at somewhat higher frequencies. In my experience, ZN448Es will invariably operate at frequencies well beyond 1 MHz. Where high speed operation is needed, it is therefore worthwhile experimenting with lower values for C2 in an attempt to find the lowest value (highest clock frequency) that gives reliable results. You may even find that the device operates without C2 included, and

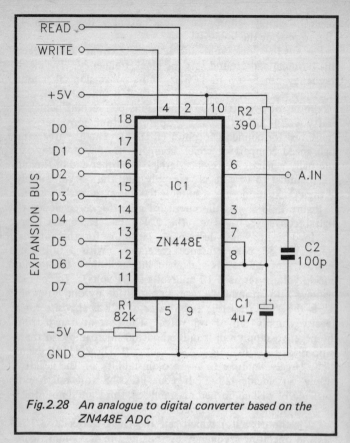

Fig.2.28 An analogue to digital converter based on the ZN448E ADC

the self-capacitance of the device, etc., will then give an operating frequency of about 2 MHz.

As explained previously, the negative write input must be driven from the address decoder, and the latter must include decoding of −IOW. Similarly, the negative read input must be fed from an address decoder which includes decoding of −IOR. The status output at pin 1 can be monitored if desired, and used to prevent premature reading of the converter. My preference is for a timing loop, which should do the job just as efficiently and simplifies the hardware slightly.

Finally

With the information provided here, anyone with a reasonable amount of experience at electronics construction should be able to interface a wide range of devices to the PC expansion bus without too much difficulty. PC interfacing is really very straightforward, and is actually much easier than interfacing to most of the eight bit computers I have dealt with (which includes practically all the popular eight bit machines). Complications can arise if wait states have to be added, but in my experience this has never been necessary. The PC expansion bus is not particularly fast, and most peripheral chips seem to be able to keep up with it. If you end up trying to add wait states, you are probably doing things the hard way, and might be better advised to have a complete rethink.

Some applications might require the added complication of using interrupts, but there are probably few PC add-ons where the use of interrupts are essential. This is a subject which is more a matter of software than hardware, and so it will not be pursued further here. Interrupts on the PC are less fraught than on most eight bit computers, but you still need to be fairly expert at the software side of things. You have to get things just right or each time the add-on is activated it will crash the computer.

Probably the best advice when designing PC add-ons is to use sensible choices for the chips that actually interface onto the expansion bus. There are plenty of integrated circuits that will easily interface with the PCs, which means that there is probably no point in using any devices which prove to be awkward.

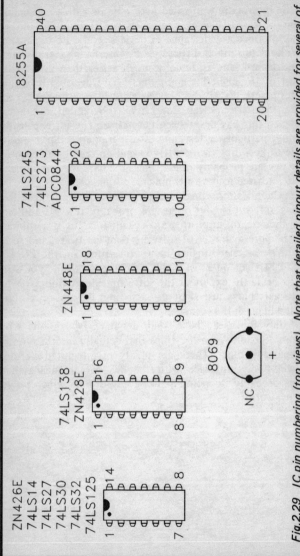

Fig.2.29 IC pin numbering (top views). Note that detailed pinout details are provided for several of these devices elsewhere in this book

80

Notes

Please note following is a list of other titles that are available in our range of Radio, Electronics and Computer books.

These should be available from all good Booksellers, Radio Component Dealers and Mail Order Companies.

However, should you experience difficulty in obtaining any title in your area, then please write directly to the Publisher enclosing payment to cover the cost of the book plus adequate postage.

If you would like a complete catalogue of our entire range of Radio, Electronics and Computer Books then please send a Stamped Addressed Envelope to:

BERNARD BABANI (publishing) LTD
THE GRAMPIANS
SHEPHERDS BUSH ROAD
LONDON W6 7NF
ENGLAND